The Divine Feminine
An Anthology of Seaside Scribes

Published as the literary arts component of
The Divine Feminine Arts Exhibition
curated by Deborah Rolig
May 2017 at
The Art League of Ocean City
Center for the Arts
Ocean City, Maryland

Literary Arts Curator and Editor, Kathleen L. Martens

For Wanda —
With admiration, appreciation
& affection

April 2020

Printed in the United States of America
Library of Congress Number: 2017940180
ISBN: 978-1-62806-128-4

Table of Contents

Acknowledgments

A resounding *thank you* to Deborah Rolig, visionary and Curator of *The Divine Feminine Arts Exhibition* who had the insight to embrace and include literary arts and this book in the spectrum of women's arts in her gallery exhibition. Her potent and creative artwork that commands the front book cover poignantly captures the elements and imagery of the *Divine Feminine*.

Our deepest gratitude to Diane Gray, artist and Co-Curator of *The Divine Feminine Arts Exhibition* for being the driving force for the overall process of coordinating and connecting all of us to collaborate on this ambitious project.

A round of applause for Rina Thaler, a zealous supporter of the arts for all and Executive Director of The Art League of Ocean City Center for the Arts for providing the opportunity to collaborate on this project, and the stellar venue for these women's stories to be told.

For her patience, responsiveness and artful touch in designing the pages of this book, *thank you,* Diane Buric, Diane Buric Design, www.DianeBuricDesign.com

Stephanie Fowler, Saltwater Media, Inc. Berlin, Maryland was a wonderful asset to the publication process, providing excellent printing services. Thank you. www.saltwatermedia.com

Our thanks to Ruth Wanberg-Alcorn for her support in connecting us with the Maryland women writers who have contributed to this anthology. Ruth established the Ocean City Library Writers group in 2009, as well as the annual *Shared Visions* collaboration between local writers and The Ocean City Center for the Arts.

A debt of gratitude to Maribeth Fischer, Executive Director of the Rehoboth Beach Writers Guild who has electrified the literary arts in our community for over a decade, making Southern Coastal Delaware a Mecca for writers. She has inspired and taught many of the authors in this book to be prolific and to hone their craft.

Much thanks to Judy Catterton, Ellen Collins, Mimi Dupont, and Christy Briedis, members of the Rehoboth Beach Writers Guild who volunteered their proofreading and support to this whirlwind publication process.

A heartfelt thanks to all of the seaside authors from Delaware and Maryland who shared their creativity to make this book possible in the fast and furious world of publishing.

And thank you to the spirit of the *divine feminine* that inhabits every page of this book.

Preface

Every creative endeavor begins as a dream, something that pulls at you, taps your shoulder until you turn your head, pay attention, respond to the call and breathe life into it. Artist Deborah Rolig, Curator of *The Divine Feminine Arts Exhibition* has had the seed of this undertaking in her head and heart for years—the idea of curating a women's arts show that explores the full spectrum of womanhood through the visual arts, and uniquely includes the literary arts.

In May of 2017, her dream came to fruition at The Art League of Ocean City, Center for the Arts, Ocean City, Maryland; and this publication manifested as the literary arts exhibit among the disciplines celebrated in the month-long women's arts event.

"The unifying theme, "Divine Feminine," revolves around the empowerment of women through honest expression, speaking from the heart," said Curator, Deborah Rolig.

Honored by Ms. Rolig and Co-Curator Diane Gray to shepherd this anthology, I was swept up in an immediate and palpable energy that burst forth from women writers living in the coastal area of Southern Delaware and Maryland—an area that has become a Mecca for writers over the past decades. My call for submissions resulted in a delightful and powerful collaboration of diverse women authors who contemplated and wrote about "The Divine Feminine."

As the pieces rolled into my inbox, the publication seemed to magically fall into place, reflecting that broad spectrum of the experiences and passages of a woman's life that Ms. Rolig had originally envisioned—women celebrating the commonality and connection with "The Divine Feminine." My concept to include works from emerging writers to seasoned authors of all ages came together—from a young poet who seeks to use literary art as therapy; to a woman reinventing herself in mid-life; to an aging woman who shares her memories and wisdom; and to women pondering our posterity and our past. Each short story, essay and poem stands alone, yet together the collection captures the meaning of The Divine Feminine.

I laughed, related and empathized as the stories and messages unfolded— like taking a journey down a radiant and sometimes irreverent rabbit hole into the essence of the feminine experience.

The personal narratives behind the stories and poems that are nestled between these pages are rich and worthy of another book—emerging writers who were inspired to pen a first publication-worthy piece, a timely poetic tribute to a dear friend lost to cancer, intimate glimpses from the charm of childhood to the memories of maidens, women in the workplace, female friendship, love, loss, and the wisdom of aging.

To complete the circle of giving, all profits from the sale of this anthology will be contributed to charities benefitting women and the arts.

This anthology speaks passionately from the heart, boldly from the head, and directly from The Divine Feminine.

Kathleen L. Martens
Literary Arts Curator and Editor

I Hear Their Voices

on my drive home from memoir class
from weekend workshops

they offer
their pages on folding tables

whisper   I'm not really a writer
or   I'm saying this wrong

they create metaphors
that gut me

abeyant women
who have put poetry and story

on hold
to cook school lunches

to care for failing husbands
or mothers with Alzheimer's

their rhythms
beat in my chest at free writes

they break my heart
at poetry readings

they shrink themselves
shrug their shoulders

against our praise

Gail Braune Comorat

The Pull of It

Marjorie F. Weber

How do you explain it, the pull of it, why 40 of us gathered three times a week without fail in that expansive room on the top floor of Sanborn Hall for orchestra practice?

You close your eyes and you are 19, in college again. It is Thursday night; the clock is ticking past 9:00. Time to go. You are tired, the room is hot and Mr. Olson, conducting, taps the music stand and holds up his arms for another go. The orchestra repeats the same passage all of you have already played at least nine times before. The rhythm is off. He frowns.

You tuck your violin under your chin and bow, squinting at the music, leaning forward towards your stand. Did you get that difficult run of 16th notes? No. Did you lose the beat? Yes. Are you bowing in sync with the other violinists? Adjust. Quick, hurry, turn the page or you and your stand mate will miss the first violins' entrance, next page, third bar coming up. Oh no, you're off key here. Slide your third finger up the string, just a tad.

Your back aches. Isn't it time to quit yet? Four beat rest. You glance again at the clock.

Then, you come upon it, that lyrical line, a repeated theme, a graceful interlude that imbues the whole piece with beauty, the genius of the composer. You know the sound of every instrument, you listen for the honeyed gold of the French Horn rising above the orchestra, the quick high notes of the flute playing counterpoint, the reedy voice of the oboe cutting through, answering, then first violins, high and sweet, joining in, echoing the melody. It's the fragment you've been waiting to hear all night and you are lost in it, surrounded by sound, all harmony, all joy, that in-the-now, nothing-else-exists-but-this-moment kind of joy you feel in the presence of such beauty, such art. And, awed, you think just then, as you have every time you have ever played this, that someone thought of this, someone created this from nothing.

It left me breathless. It always does.

~~~~~~~~~~*~~~~~~~~~~

These Hands

are stubby they could never
play piano or swing a partner with style
they are gnarled can't make a fist or wear
fancy rings these hands are strong   they
yanked dandelions   plucked chickens
when they were just a kid   hoisted
a Duluth pack   paddled up-stream
held onto a job and a marriage
at the same time   these hands
are pliable cradled a baby in one
a protest banner in the other
these hands are free
of   men who said they couldn't
play soccer run for the Senate or climb
the ladder unless they slept
with the boss or stayed single
until they were too old to have kids.

Sherri Wright

———————❋———————

These Feet

these feet are stubby
they could never learn to dance
or skip rope with rhythm   these feet
are wide   they don't fit into stilettos
these feet are strong   they
hiked a mountain carrying a body heavy with
the daughter who wasn't born
these feet spread to give her birth
they rocked her to sleep
these feet are powerful   they ran
a marathon twelve times   these feet
are free   they stomped
out of a marriage
and never looked back

Sherri Wright

Molting

Kathleen L. Martens

The early beach sun creeps up over my deck railing and spills liquid gold into my art space. It's quiet, except for the incessant tick-tick of the Thomas Tompion clock on the mantle and the scrape of my palette knife across the canvas. The cadence of the minutes passing echoes in my vaulted ceiling—and I paint. I stroke, press, and drag my brush until the blue paint oozes and leaves the perfect thick and thin lines that I somehow know will read as ripples in the waves from across the room. My wrist nods and flows like a conductor directing unheard music. I step back to see how the enlivened water eerily moves, and I smile because it works—yes, it works. It's the only time I feel my life works—here, near my love, in these still moments on the other side of the bridge.

It's the only time I feel I am in command, conducting some small part of my life away from the years of running charity events, slicing oranges for soccer games, and playing the many roles that draw my blood, my strength, my *me*. In those few precious fleeting hours in the meniscus between dark and light, night and day, in the "just befores"—just before bed and just before our beach house full of guests awakens—I molt. I drop my mantle of motherhood and wife to release the hidden artist inside me.

I should be grateful, Oprah and my meditations tell me. I should be grateful for the pin that holds me in place, like a rare butterfly, for everyone to admire. I'm not; I'm desperately lonely, while relentlessly surrounded.

Even though we arrived late last night after the usual frantic Friday escape into traffic, I am up before dawn. I leave my husband snoring in the darkened room, and move my silent feet down the cold hardwood steps to prepare to see my "Mr. O," as I've come to call him. I have no guilt for this uncontrollable love affair with the ocean and the shore. It is an irrepressible passion. I always think of him, close my eyes, and smile unashamedly—even while sitting next to my husband, Daniel, in our overloaded SUV at the top of the Bay Bridge.

I can feel the ocean comforting me, listening to the whispers of my soul. It never fails to free me, and I feel myself transform, casting off my shell of perfection—the perfect mother, the perfect wife—to walk barefoot in the sand with unkempt hair, unpolished toes, and dreams of a life free to be myself with Mr. O. He likes the raw me, the real me, the me before the messages took hold that told me how to be, the me before my life of tennis whites at country clubs and hair swept back in bows.

I think of the Old Masters whose apprentices did all the painting while the Master took credit for the final piece. I feel like that, never holding a brush to create the details of my own life, only appearing in the end, to add my name on the bottom right corner to signify this was my creation. But, it wasn't handmade by me, I confess. It was made by the hands of others: my children, my husband, even a five-pound puppy that made his paw marks on the canvas of my life.

For now, I luxuriate alone with my brushes and the acrid scent of the oils on my palette: six shades of blue, three greens, a touch of red, and some golden yellows for her hair. I mix just the right shade with an urgent tapping of my brush, with one ear listening to the lapping sounds from the open window that call to me, and the other for the footsteps and flushes in the ceiling above. I take in the selfish aroma of my one-cup hazelnut Keurig, not wanting to wake them with the alluring scent of a full brewed pot. I raise my shoulders, not yet ready for the clarion call to relinquish my selfish time in my secret world, to take on the cloak of mother, the role of wife, the demands of host, queen of the beach house.

I'm conflicted, wanting the morning to move on so I can see him in the new light, but I don't want my creative process to be rushed. After all, it's from the ocean that I've learned to set my boundaries, demand my space, and feel my worth. I've learned it, although I've yet to live it. He's strong, dependable, and steadfast, yet he allows his natural moods to flow freely with no apology. I need to learn to do that; I adapt myself to suit the moods of others.

I work wherever I please on the canvas, unfettered in my rare freedom, and she takes shape. Surfacing from the blotches of color, she flashes the shimmering scales on her tail, and her blond hair with bits of shell and tiny fish dances on the canvas with wild abandon. The foam and bubbles push her forward in the powerful flow of the sea that surrounds her. It makes her reach out, unashamed of her nakedness, as if she could swim into your arms. I angle the easel closer to the emerging natural light, and add a final touch of glimmer to her captivating green eyes, quickly cleaning up a tiny splatter of oily evidence from my immaculate wide-plank hardwood floors. Her look comes together—tender, enticing, yet pure and full of heart. My own heart beats faster, and I inhale deeply. It's good, no, it's very good, I tell myself, and I push aside my usual self-doubt.

Tonight, I'm throwing a party for my seventieth birthday and our forty-fifth anniversary. It's our summer's requisite hoorah. Even my birthday is over-shadowed by my husband. He isn't to blame; he is just as much a victim of this life of routines and rules, this cardboard box we share. It's all he's ever known. I'll order this and arrange that, and celebrate myself and the years of birthing and bonding to this man who gave me his name. Waiting on friends, cooking, cleaning, I'll toast my seven decades living as a crustacean who has never learned to molt.

I think of the quote that inspired me to paint this seaside siren that calls desperately to me to live out loud, to find my true self, to audaciously create in broad daylight. "I must be a mermaid," Anaïs Nin wrote. "I have no fear of depths and a great fear of shallow living." Yet, I still paint in shadow, thinking my true self would not be welcomed in my daylight world.

I have lived in this fear of shallow for all of my adult years, so why did I succumb to the demands of my affluent suburban life? I was enticed by the neatness of it all, the comfort of the rules, knowing just what to say and do, with marker pen poised to slash the white space from my children's calendars. I should be grateful for this safe and perfect life with perfect shoes.

Her face has come clear now with the final touch of my brush. She wears a look of serenity that I don't share except in these precious, guilty, stolen moments when everyone sleeps and no one asks me: "What's to eat?" "Where's my suit?" "There's a button missing; can you sew it on?" "Where'd I put my keys?" "Can I borrow the car?"

I rip off my painting shirt and store it with my mermaid in my secret place. Someone has brought a puppy without permission. He stretches, and lumbers to my side. His tiny sharp tooth lodges itself in the leg of my yoga pants, signaling it's time to go. He drags along behind me, and I pry his little jaw open and release him. The symbolism doesn't elude me. I open the sliding screen door and silently close the latch. The whine of the little dog and the first upstairs flush fade behind me, and I'm free just in time.

The salted air lures my hurried barefoot steps along the dunes to the south end of the boardwalk. With my water sandals swinging in my hands, I stop to fill my lungs with salty anticipation. For good luck, I touch the rough gray splintering railing that marks the boardwalk's end, and my fingers register the feel of its ridged and rugged texture. I save it in my memory for my art.

I notice that my blue, size-small "Life is Good" T-shirt is stretched tight across my middle. Some weakness this season has made me surrender too often to the long-forgotten beach food; I have returned to Thrasher's. The punishing gulls swoop down to attack my familiar oversized salted cup of fries scented with apple cider vinegar, trying to prevent my sin, screeching, "No, No, No!"

I have much to ask Mr. O today. He's always there to listen to my aching heart, and today I need his wisdom. I need his arms around me. I fear I am disappearing into a dark place. I pick up my pace. One mile of boardwalk exercise, then my illicit escape awaits me, I tell myself. I slip on my shoes and hypnotize myself with the thumping sound on the boards beneath my impatient feet. A sticky glob of ice cream, a stray Funland ticket, and a Dolle's saltwater taffy wrapper connect me with my jealousy, thoughts of husbands who don't golf all weekend and dreams of mothers who don't plan their own birthdays, but then I think, I do it so well. My tears begin.

I stop to pick up a lost hermit crab, its natural shell decorated with the painted helmet of a Redskins player. I know what it feels like to live beneath a label. His claws neatly line up like fingers on a praying hand, and he pulls back in embarrassment, as if he feels my eyes on him. The smell of dying rises up from his shell, and I reach through the boardwalk railing to place the escapee on some dune grass with hope.

I have my love in my sights in the distance beyond a rounded wall of sand that was sucked up from the ocean floor in one of his unexpected moods last night. I turn right and follow the winding fenced-in path. I am almost there. I run to him, my wonderful ocean. He thunders today at the sight of me. Unlike my husband's moods, he doesn't make me pull into my own shell. He allows me to be real, and to bravely bring to him whomever I am each day. It's a freedom I feel with no one else, except maybe Helen, my best art college girlfriend, who accepts me as I am but lives a freer life and struggles to relate.

I am alone along the early shore, empty as far as I can see, two far-off concrete towers half-wrapped in morning shadows like paper around an ice cream cone. I feel some brief relief as my feet sink into the cool sand. I watch a horseshoe crab soothe itself in a cooling massage of foam, encrusted with dependent travelers—shells, barnacles, and tiny misled crustaceans clinging for dear life, like me. I nudge it until it catches the current of a rescuing wave.

Something is different today. I am being swallowed by all the expectations in my life. The errand-filled planning of my own party opened a wound in me that has been festering all week. The sun is pushing through the bank of gray along the horizon. It's a westerly insistent wind that lifts white wisps from the crest of each wave, and I see Mr. O is also in an agitated mood. Still, he will always listen, so constant, so deep in his understanding.

He often leaves me with a feeling of resolve that melts like the secret cup of Kohr's custard that I sometimes indulge in on my walks home. The sugar high readies my lioness to leap. Each time I enter my door, my courage to change somehow dissipates, and I keep my paintings and my feelings locked up like a secret lover in a closet where no one goes. Instead, I take out the frying pans to prepare the brunch—omelets for 13, me and the two-dozen sets of sunburned legs and arms sprawling on white organic cotton sheets upstairs.

Today is different; I've reached a point. Walking beside him and confiding in him isn't enough. I've never actually gone in the ocean in all the time I've used him as my secret confidant. I've never let go of my fussy concerns about the cold, getting my hair wet, the grit, the undertow, the excuses that prevent me from feeling him raw and real. I step lightly through a half-moon of old crushed memories, broken chards and shells left behind by the tide. Only one familiar woman and her curly-haired white dog are in the distance, too far away to see my sin.

A sudden blanket of foam sizzles over my feet, draws back, and I follow. Ankles, calves, knees, and the swell of my belly chilled by his hands make me hesitate, but he entreats me. My feet lift off the coarse bottom. I turn to see the watery arc above me and I give in, pulled under by his power. Sun, churning sand, I'm tumbled in the foaming bubbles, my long graying hair, like my mermaid's tresses, dancing in the restless water. I feel my breath needing to escape, to be replenished, yet I stay, marveling at the sound of the pounding waves, caught in the hydraulic of confusion.

I am drawn farther and farther from my contrived life, and I'm transformed into the woman I was—hopeful, youthful, creative, unfettered and alive. I see my tail growing and shimmering with blue-green scales, my youthful breasts lifted by the current, my long silky hair with bits of shell and tiny fish playing joyfully around it like an alluring coral shelf.

I feel the current taking me deeper. His desire for me pulls me farther out, and I succumb to the freedom. I watch the bubbles of my final breath rise up above me to the surface. I see my daughter's pleading eyes, my son's search along the shore, my grandchildren's tears, my husband's regretful face changing with kind promises, my friends begging me to love them enough to stay. The sun reaches through the water surrounding me, and I rise up with a sudden understanding. I push my way through the final crushing wave that holds me, and it pulls off my mermaid tail, freeing my legs.

My cheek rests in the gentle foam, safely on the sand, and my rapid breath slows. My hand lies next to a set of bird footprints, and my eyes follow their silly drunken tracks that wander off in any direction, at their whim. Nature is so wise, I think.

I walk along the shore for hours, gathering stares in my disheveled state, meandering where I please. I'm not concentrating, just giving myself time to absorb. I'm boldly molting in broad daylight.

The sun goes high, turns down toward the horizon again, and urges me to return. I walk up onto the deck of my oceanfront home. When did the cedar shakes turn from silver to brown, I wonder? Imperceptibly, over time, just as I had slowly weathered? Just as my husband has slowly gone bald? I am the reverse; my aging has turned my sandy brown to silver beneath my camouflage of blond.

I look through the sliding doors and I see them standing silent, staring— the entire gang. I imagine how I must look. I don't care. Even the caterer is frozen in place, waiting for the tap of my baton. My nervous guests are dressed so stylishly, champagne in hand, standing in my precious pre-dawn art space that has magically turned into the family room again.

"Bridget, where *were* you?" Daniel steps out behind me and talks through teeth under his breath. "The guests are here; they're hungry," he says through a smile intended for those watching at a distance, but not for me. I laugh to think there is $100 worth of food per person, waiting within reach just over the granite counter, to save them from starvation. My perfect husband stands tanned, tall, and trim. I smile. I am not the only one who suffers from the disease of perfection. "Have you seen yourself? Have you looked in the mirror?" he asks.

I think the same, have you, have *we*? "You were worried about me weren't you?" I translate, touching his face. Without a word, I walk across the room, and drag out my easel from the storage closet. I dramatically whip off the cover, which is actually my daughter's forty-year-old baby sheet.

My friends and family draw in their breaths and everyone applauds.
"Oh, it's beautiful."
"Spectacular."
"Is that your gift from Daniel?"
"Oh my, Daniel, where did you get it?"
"Who is the artist?"
"Do you mind sharing? I have to have one of his works for
  my collection!"
They examine my painting, step back, and then lean forward with concentrated appreciation. They are silenced by her look. My mermaid emerges from the blue and green of the windy sea with arms that promise to hold

you, heal you, love you as you are. The water moves and undulates around her. Her vibrant green eyes look deep, catch the light just right, and electrify her admirers.

My friend Helen, the only one who knows my secret, walks toward the painting, which is as tall as she. "Well, let's see," she says, and winks at me, an understanding gesture that makes me glad to be alive. She bends over to examine the lower right-hand corner. "Bridget King McDaniel," she reads, in six distinct syllables, and I feel the last of my shell peel away and clatter to the floor.

I accept a loving hug and kiss from Helen, who kindly plucks a length of seaweed from my wild hair. In my peripheral view, I see my children's faces, lit with amazement, and watch Daniel walk toward me with a look I haven't seen in many years. He studies me intensely with wonder, and his eyes flicker, searching mine.

"Danny." I smile, calling him by his college nickname to instantly rewind us in time. I so desperately need him to remember two imperfect, optimistic dreamers: he, the dedicated architect who rebuilt villages after earthquakes, and me, the promising artist who secretly painted colorful seaside murals on dreary city walls. Can he see himself tenderly plucking that dab of turquoise paint from my hair nearly half a century ago? Can he remember the deep connection and convictions we once had? He glances at the painting and then at me, and pauses for a painful minute.

Tick-tick-tick is the only rebounding sound, and I wait. Then, he shakes his head, grinning, and I know he sees me. He looks through the mess that I've become—weathered beauty, unknown artist, shells and tiny fish in my hair—to see his mermaid. He steps forward and kisses me with lips that taste of long ago. All along it was I who had to change, to change my world around me. I am the artist of my own life now, and I step back and smile because it works; yes, it works.

"Molting" won a Judge's Choice Award in the Rehoboth Beach Reads Short Story Contest and was first published in *Beach Days* by Cat and Mouse Press in 2015.

~~~~~~~✳~~~~~~~

The Islander

She—wholly suited to her beachcombing life—
adores the scratchy sand and all its treasures,
revels in its coarse, clinging, feel.

The touch of cold surf on her feet,
—still aflame from sprint to water's edge—
titillates her.

Distant shadows,
in the on-coming waves,
both intrigue and stimulate her.

She explores the island's marshland,
plays with its black ooze
as it slurps up, like oil,
between her wiggling toes.

The smell of the place
infuses her body and captures her soul
—even before she understands its hold.

…in the beginning, this is her playground,
everything here a favored toy.
Then, it becomes more…
Even the casual observer
can detect her joy at being, precisely
where she belongs.

With windswept hair, fanning out like wings,
wrinkled by the salty breeze, she stands,
overlooking her home.

Her skin soft, smooth,
pelted by the pumice
of miniscule particles captured and thrown
by blasts of sandy air,
her eyes, in constant smile,
pinched, partly in protection, mostly

in happiness, for
she lives a simple island-life and asks
for nothing more.

Sometimes she digs her dinner,
dozens of clams, and, instead of ritually
returning to the kitchen to consume her tasty meal,
this reaper shucks them on the spot,
swallows their juice and gem
so they become another essential part of her
living dream.

She accepts the individual elements—the wind, the water—
and respects the force of their unpredictable marriages,
their inescapable affairs.

At times, barefooted, blinded by tears,
she battles changing tides and raging floods,
as violent storms seek, again and again,
to reclaim the land she loves.

In prayer and deed, this loyal islander fiercely fights for her place
on the eroding strip of sand she calls home
…and, again, she wins!
Aged now, yet beautifully weathered,
self-sustained, but God-directed, she humbly reigns,
this side of heaven, in her isolated kingdom
between the ocean's vastness and her
beloved bay.

Ruth M. Alcorn

Insignificance

I sit, only a speck,
at the foot of ocean's vastness,
on the boards.

Waves barely hiss,
sand silently tracks each trespasser,
the distant sun offers light, yet little warmth, as
wind makes nose and cheek feel alive,
then numb.
Serenity embraces me as I gaze toward the watery east.

Except for obvious signs of the present,
this could be a glance into distant past,
or a vision of time to come...

My eyes distract my mind
to watch faded red tripods plot their route;
pigeons mark their place; their heads
dot, point, stab past strollers, stragglers.

These gamely creatures
shimmer as they walk, stop for handouts,
cautiously cry for more—
evermore.

Here too other seekers of good fortune,
tick along,
spend time,
search for memories
to complete their life.

Distant noises reverberate
as builders restore eroded strips of beach
and bury deeper yet this island's natural treasures...

Ruth M. Alcorn

Female Friends?
Consider the Possibilities

Mary Leach

Females can't be friends. Women are their own worst enemies. Everybody knows that. Put two or three females together and within days—or minutes—they'll be fighting. Over men, if single, widowed or divorced. Over child-raising or not. If she stays home to raise her children she's a slacker, if she goes out to work she's neglecting her babies or teenagers when they most need their mothers, if she chooses or is unable to have children she's not doing her womanly duty, if married—if not married, that's a whole 'nuther story. Over jobs and money. She's an Affirmative Action hire; she makes too much for a woman, and God-forbid having a woman as a boss—pure chaos. And yet, who but a woman really understands another woman.

Consider the movie *Hidden Figures*. On the surface it's an inspiring story about three black females who work for NASA in Tidewater Virginia in the late 1950's and who prove, against all odds, that black women can succeed—more or less—in what is a very white and very male environment. They do it by being smarter and working harder than just about anyone else, meanwhile dealing with rampant and disgusting segregation, that among other things, forces one of the heroines to walk—run really—nearly one-half mile in high heels (*de rigueur* at the time) simply to use 'colored facilities.'

There is the obligatory white Queen Bee who revels in her superior status by discriminating against the three black women until she is forced by the white male group leader to recognize their collective talents. The movie ends with the three triumphant—one even beats the new-fangled IBM computer in speed and accuracy, while another teaches herself how to program the thing and a third forces her way into a university program formerly open only to whites and becomes the nation's first African-American female aeronautical engineer.

The film is indeed about three individuals achieving remarkable success by dint of their own talents in a very unwelcoming world. But not far under the surface of that story is the fact that the three women are not rivals—rather they rely on a very strong friendship bond to help one another with transportation, child care, praise in the workplace, and even—being Hollywood—finding a man for the widowed 'computer' whose mother makes life possible by caring for her children while she supports her family. Those women individually confront and conquer stereotypes, but they are able to do so because each gets by 'with a little help from her friends.'

Or consider the very long-running TV series, *The Golden Girls*. Individually the three actresses, Bea Arthur, Rue McClanahan and Betty White enjoyed career (and in the case of 95-year-old Betty White continue to enjoy) careers that played to type. Bea Arthur's *Maude* was terrific as the foil and emasculator of that arch misogynist Archie Bunker. Rue McClanahan was the superbly bitchy Aunt Fran of *Mama's Family*. And Betty White was the rather lewd and always impossible to deal with Sue Ann Nivens on *The Mary Tyler Moore Show*. But as *Golden Girls*, while their individual personae came through loud and clear, it was the loving friendship and mutual tolerance of their individual foibles that arguably makes the show a hit that continues to be played on cable channels virtually everywhere.

From its earliest days, women friends have been central to TV sitcoms. Lucy may have been married to Desi, but where would that redheaded screwball have been without Ethel to keep her from getting into too much hot water. Or, for that matter, Mary Richards without Rhoda when grumpy Mr. Grant or manipulative Phyllis Lindstrom (there's that Queen Bee again) made Mary's life difficult.

Art, and especially television, arguably that most plebian of arts, imitates life. While women's history has been neglected until relatively recently, it is pretty clear that women leaders—like the women who founded religious orders, hospitals, colleges and social welfare organizations—had strong women friendships. Where would Susan B. Anthony have been in the struggle for Women's Suffrage without Elizabeth Cady Stanton? Or Eleanor Roosevelt without the abiding friendship of Lorena Hickok, her beloved 'Hick'. While FDR's relationships with Lucy Mercer Rutherford and Missy LeHand are well known, it was Hick and her other women friends at Hyde Park to whom Eleanor turned for sanity when her husband's behavior and especially his death in Hot Springs, Georgia in the arms of Lucy Mercer were particularly painful for a woman who had to live so much of her life in the public eye.

Legend has not always been kind to women in groups. If powerful, they're Amazons, who seek to destroy humankind, or Scylla and Charybdis, who jointly use their sirens' calls to lure sailors to their death. If perceived as weak, they and their children (presumably the result of virgin births since men bear no responsibility) are viewed as a burden on society, a charge on the parish. If they try to organize for better pay (women comprise 47% of the workforce, but still earn considerably less than men in equivalent positions), they are viewed as 'other' and too often seen as unwomanly who should return to their proper roles of *kinde, kuche, kirche*.

And yet, times they are a-changin'. While coffee-klatches may not dot the suburban landscape as they once did—women are mostly in the workplace after all, so 10 AM encounters with other mothers whose children are in school may not be possible, women's investment clubs and book clubs, with or without Oprah's urging, are everywhere. Hotels and airlines are encouraging women to go on holidays with friends and setting up excursions toward that end. And a personal favorite, social media has gotten into the act. Along with Harmony and Match.com, there is now a website—*Girlfriend Social*—where one can search for friends.

Women may still be teased for going to the bathroom in groups, but who else but a friend will guard the door when the lock doesn't work, hand you some toilet tissue when there isn't any in your cubicle, warn you about spinach in your teeth or a skirt that's caught up in your clothing, or (thanks Rosanna Danna of *Saturday Night Live* fame) toilet paper caught on your shoe. And for those of us who hate missing the beginning of the second act because of 1500 seat theaters with four stall women's restrooms where at least one stall is virtually guaranteed to be inoperable, joining together for Potty Parity is virtually a must. *Sisterhood is Powerful* after all.

Not too many years ago around Christmas time many of us received and proudly wore T-shirts and sweat shirts, which proclaimed that if Three Wise Women had visited Bethlehem, they would have asked for directions, arrived on time, swept the stable, brought casseroles and cared for the infant so that the Blessed Mother could get some much needed rest. AMEN: The power and glory of women friends—the Divine Feminine—in word and deed.

✳

A Trilogy in Memory of Jane

Hungry Ghosts

Don't let them do that to me, you said,
when we laughed at an obituary full of
flowery sentimental stuff.

Forget the color teal and don't describe me as a survivor, you said.

No neat boxes for you,
I promised. But it wasn't time.
We had three, maybe four years.
Not enough,
before the demons circled. Closer.

In your poems, you grappled with the mysteries of dying, and
threaded the pearls of your suffering.
Tumors, scans, surgery, chemotherapy, baldness.
But with your signature wit,

you called the cancer "The Hungry Ghosts Eating My Insides."

For seven years and six months you kept the ghosts at bay.
We had our last martini at your daughter's wedding,
six months before you died.

Three olives, you said.

Sayonara

In August, for your 70th birthday, I gave you a bathing suit cover-up.
Blue and white striped.
We both knew you'd never wear it.
The looming shadows had edged closer, encircled.
The ghosts, no longer placated, did their work:
nausea vomiting constipation diarrhea liver failure jaundice sepsis…
You fought back until you couldn't, anymore. With grace,
you acquiesced. Morphine, comfort. No more pain.

End of September. Waning sun, wilting flowers, decay setting in.
It was time. Our last visit. I held your cold hands.
Your eyes, locked on mine, behind
your purple glasses, now
too large on your gaunt face.
You were ready for your departure.

Done with fighting. But still you. Fully present, undimmed.

You sat in your Barcalounger;
an amused smile illuminated your face.
You waved your arms back and forth,
weaving, as you sang Sayonara,
Sayonara.
As if it was a surprise you had planned.
You laughed. I joined in.
Our last laugh, irreverent. As always. Still you.

Raw-bleak-icy-desolate, I pleaded, unspoken
Don't leave me.
"I'll be waiting for you on the moon,"
you said.

Another hug, a last "I love you," then,
the final moment. I stood. Edged away
from you.
We waved, a slow-motion wave, as if
a normal visit, a normal good-bye.
I stood at the door,
until your face began to blur.

Five days later, you died. September 25th.
A Sunday, at around midnight.

The next night, the moon gazed
down at me. In the silence of your absence
I whispered, "Anam Cara.
Soul Friend."
That's what we called each other.

I waved and blew a kiss.

The Plain Truth

I didn't say the word, teal, or survivor, or speak of your death
in honeyed clichés.

I didn't talk of how we would laugh, until we couldn't stop, until
we almost peed.

I had to speak of your warmth and incandescence. How you
 radiated goodness and generosity.   Abundance and spaciousness.

I had to mention your grace, courage,
and perseverance   as you fought
the insistent ravenous ghosts.

How even in your last days,
after you surrendered, when death neared,
serenity and peace   flowed from you.

And your tinkling laughter, as you sang Sayonara.
I had to tell them that.

In one of your poems you asked, "What is the secret of dying well?"
In the last lines, you told us.

"Why do you make it so hard?
The plain truth is in the
snow-covered garden
and
the spring green shoot."

Margaret Kirby

Dying to Ask

Slightly East of Eden
living on an island
I ask the 799 other
suffering souls
most of them
born here
What is the secret
of dying well?
Diminishing fear?
Evolution of compassion?
Expanded consciousness then?
Vibrations of love energy?
O Come on they say
Why do you make it so hard?

The plain truth is in the
snow covered garden
and
the spring green shoot

Jane O'Rourke Bender (March 2015)

Submitted by Margaret Kirby
In loving memory of her friend, Jane O'Rourke Bender, August 4, 1946–September 25, 2016

Tonight

There is a woman tonight in the Sudan, in Paris, in Botswana, or in the Mississippi delta who watches someone curl up on his bed, a thin shape almost insubstantial under the covers. She wants him to laugh with her, to ask her to dance. She wishes she wanted to dance with him. She would be happy if he just walked and felt himself grounded on the earth, sensed its solidity, listening with the soles of his feet to the reverberations of all the other people stepping on the earth at that moment.

There is a woman tonight who looks at the moon's luminous flat face, who sees it climb above the city rooftops, above the forest canopy, above the long-grass prairie, or above jagged ice mountains, and reaches out her hand to touch its distant glow.

There is a woman tonight in a barrio, on a farm, in a penthouse, on a park bench, who feels as if she is the only woman in the world, as separate from all others as one star is from the millions of other stars in the infinite universe.

And there is also a woman tonight in a small room in a small house in a small town who feels her breath, the rise and fall of it, who hears the sound it makes in her throat, in the pulsing silence, who knows it keeps her alive, who suddenly understands that as she breathes so does every other woman in the world, that it is their breathing that connects them like ribbons spun from light.

Ellen Collins

———————✳———————

Shelf Life

Carole Schauer

Who are you and what do you want? These questions have been asked across the centuries and deliberated by philosophers, both great and small. The amount of discussion and written word given to these topics is probably more than one can imagine. But there is one additional query that could propel one to formulating and crystallizing one's responses to these questions. The added query creates a lens that could help one leave behind that which is extraneous and uncertain. That question is, "What if you knew the date you are to die?"

Knowing this date is like having a "sell by date" found on an item in a grocery store. This date indicates when the product should be removed by the store from the shelf; in other words, it is the end or expiration of its shelf life. Having an ending shelf life date stamped on my life, perhaps on my forehead, could greatly alter the way I look at my future.

In thinking and worrying *ad infinitum* about who I am and what I want, I think of those things I hope to do, accomplish or change in the coming days, months and years of my life. At times, these items make it on to "to do" lists that often remain unfinished. But what would I do with the rest of my life if I knew I had a short shelf life?

Will I actually end my procrastination and undertake the items on my bucket list? Will I stop dawdling and make amends with those where relationships are broken? Will I make the improvements to my home that have long been on my mind? Will I give of my time and talents in a substantial way at a local charity to help those in need, while at the same time practicing the tenets of my faith? Will I finish my genealogy research and write up the findings as well as my family stories? Will I have the time to do these things if I suddenly learn that my shelf life date looms in the near future?

Perhaps rather than considering the "what ifs" in my future that suggest a negative view point like that of the glass that is half empty, I should live as if the glass is half full. If who I am is defined by what I do and not what I hope to do, should I not live my life as if it were ending today, no matter if I have another five, ten or twenty years in front of me? Should not my credos be, "Be the best you can be," "Do all the good you can today," and "Live in a way that you can look back at yesterday and say I have no regrets." If I lived that way, you can see who I am by what I do, and knowing one's shelf life would not make a difference because it would always be today.

———~~~~~✳~~~~~———

Divine Feminine–The Significance

Maeke Ermarth

Who or what is divine? Who or what is feminine? Answers differ depending on who is being asked. Clear that from my mind. Focus on me. What do the words "divine" and "feminine" bring to my mind and, particularly, what does *my* mind evince when the words are placed together—divine feminine?

Divine, to me, conjures up being godlike, miraculous or, at the very least, extraordinarily different yet benevolent. Feminine is to be anatomically female or possessing the characteristics—positive or negative—society has identified as being female. People worldwide easily recognize Mother Mary, Mother Theresa and Florence Nightingale as valued examples of divine and feminine.

Historically, St. Paul the apostle told a congregation that all believers are saints, and he made no reference to gender. I will not argue his statement. In fact, I will go even beyond "believers" and say that I believe the divine and feminine exist within *every* woman. To release them, she needs only to recognize them and follow their paths.

One amazing feat that separates the boys from the girls is the females' unique ability to incubate, nourish, and produce life. Beyond the physical ability to do so, women in general possess this ability metaphorically as well. They incubate and nourish the seeds within all of us and help bring forth our inner selves that otherwise might forever remain dormant. Such was the case with our childhood maid in Florida, Freddie Mae, during the era when segregation still existed but was on the proper path to its decline.

Freddie Mae was the first *divine feminine* I endeared, and she will forever feel like my lifeline to the world. I never knew her last name, but the name is insignificant; it is her soul and influence that were—and are to this day. When Freddie Mae was present, so was Respect, Wisdom and Calm. While working quietly and innocuously in the background, she had total command and control of the household; and yet, she was able to give us the illusion that we did. Oh, the grace of her courtesy toward and her insight into all the dynamics surrounding her were treasured gifts! Being the youngest of three girls, I had the privilege of spending much of her working day in her presence where I experienced the greatest classroom of all time. Just being near her made me feel safe, proud of myself, and hungry for the qualities and smarts she possessed.

"Never apologize for nor feel guilty or ashamed of whom you are" was the mantra she insisted I sear into my heart and soul. She also instructed me not to be pompous because everyone, in some fashion, is rich and worthy. Just as importantly, she always took time to listen to me and allowed herself to be approachable with anything in or on my heart. When elated, she shared my joy and happiness. When puzzled, she shared my confusion. When hurt, she felt my pain. Between her nurturing my belief in God due to a childhood encounter with Him—that my own mother excused as me seeing shadows from trees outside, but Freddie Mae never doubted or questioned my life-altering experience—and her arms always open to receive me so long as I was sincere and without malice. I still believe to this day she was an angel placed before me as a figure to emulate since I was/am female and she, most assuredly, was divine.

Throughout my life I have been blessed with the acquaintances and friendships of many "sisters" who were and are also divine feminine. I have had many callings in my life that I believe are divine, and I know without a doubt that being feminine has produced good results when I attempt to answer the calls. My biological father used to tell us girls, "If you want to be successful in life: Act like a woman, but think like a man." When I think back on the more prominent female influences in my life, those ladies most assuredly fit my father's definition of a successful woman.

Divinity cuts both ways. Femininity not so much. I believe each gender has a tad of the other in terms of mind and spirit; however, I also believe that the *masculine* and *feminine* will forever remain distinctly autonomous yet powerful. Therein explains why I have extracted long-held feelings and thoughts from people who would not have been so forthcoming with a "brother." It also explains why I take some of my concerns to "sisters" who I know can carry a torch and obtain positive results. Many qualities are unique to the divine and the feminine. It behooves me to recognize and honor them. We who are feminine need to embrace the qualities of the feminine *and* the divine so we, too, can respectfully bring forth and share the abilities that exist within each of us. Just as fate in a proverb whispers to a lady warrior, "You cannot withstand the storm," the lady warrior whispers back, "I *am* the storm."

How is honor to be expressed to the divine feminine in our lives and to those who came before we were even a thought? For myself, I have a pattern of adopting qualities of the divine feminine that should never die that I feel capable of incorporating into my own being.

Sometimes I am daring and will take in qualities about which I am uncertain I can model well. If successful—I keep them. If not, I let them go and hope someone less inept will take them and carry them forward.

With that, I will end this piece, go stand before a mirror and ask myself, "Am I divine feminine?" If not, I have a lot of homework to do. If I am, I have a lot of homework to continue.

*

Triple Goddess

During each of her powerful transitions she [the moon] *was portrayed as a different aspect of woman. Lunar Mystery: Woman and the Moon* by Roslyne Sophia Berlin

I. Maiden

little damsel   ardent and
       eager
she thinks her body is
       eden
       on display
she waits   cool   remains
       serene   her
countenance magnetic   she believes
       her circumference
navigable   her terrain   all
       marble silence

II. Mother

matron protector guardian
you are open
a mouth   releasing a thousand
moths at dusk   you are
a bucket spilling
water   you distrust
the days   you leave us   you
are a boomerang   obsessive
perfectionist   showing us
devotion from watchful eyes

III. Muse/Crone

We are stenciled with valleys
ruled by power lines and late-
night hotlines
lunacy twists through our veins
like endless twine
we are held together by
tender knots
pulled tight

Gail Braune Comorat

Triple Goddess was first published in "Phases of the Moon" in 2015 by Finishing Line Press

———————✳———————

I Hate Rain

Faith Lord

I hate rain! I hate wet smelly dogs that bite at my heels. I hate soggy garbage that lingers in the broken sidewalks. I hate those with cars who splash dirty gutter water onto people who must wait in the rain at the crosswalk until the light turns green. I hate Mr. Brittingham's grayed-white tee shirt that flies from the second story clothesline like a forgotten flag, and I really hate 8th grade.

"Good morning, Class," says Sister as she enters the room. "Good morning, Sis-ter Lor-et-ta." I join the regurgitation and my hands fold and my body moves into its straight-back position as instinctively as I breathe. Gosh, Sister is so beautiful!

I close my eyes and envision myself painting Sister Loretta's lips with Hazel Bishop's red fire. I also give her softly curled shoulder-length hair; it looks best flung to one side. I spit on the dry black cake in the little red mascara case, Maybelline of course, and douse the small brush in the paste. I use it to darken the lashes around Sister's almond shaped eyes. Sister has the straightest back, even for a nun. Her tiny waist and big breasts refuse to hide under the heavy black wool habit, a habit designed to reveal only an angelic face and hands ready to work for the Lord. I know a Marilyn Monroe silver-lame gown: She's too beautiful to be a nun.

Oh God, I don't want to be a nun. Father Mathias says if God calls me, I must submit or He will make my life miserable. I don't want to believe Father, and I pray to God every day reminding Him that I would make one lousy nun.

It's 10 a.m. and Sister breaks the silence of the seventy-two soldier-backed kids. They sit as ordered: hands locked in a tight embrace and feet nailed firmly to the floor. "All the girls form a paired line in the center aisle," says Sister. "Mrs. Jenson is here to help you pick the graduation dresses." I don't know why all of our dresses have to be exactly alike. Brenda, Mildred, and Lois like the blue one. It's sprinkled with those stiff white-velvet flowers. I hate it! It has a place for breasts; I don't have breasts. I wish I had a safety pin to fix my sash. I always tie it too tight and it rips out at the seam; I want a waist like Sister's; Brenda has a waist. I don't have breasts for the blue dress and I don't have a waist either.

I hate rain! Why does it have to rain? It washes away the glue that I use to hold the soles to my shoes and gushes up my newspaper innersoles. I hate girls that huddle and whisper; they think it's funny that my soles flop and slosh when I walk. My hair looks like Miss Elsie's cat after Bobby Lewis dunks it in the hole in the alley. I hate rain.

I like watching Sister. It seems she has no feet. Her long black habit stops just short of the floor. The habit lifts slightly toward the back as Sister floats from one side of the room to the other. Her slender porcelain hands support the chalk that leaves behind a perfect example of the Palmer method of writing. My ink-stained hands and face give evidence of my losing battle with my pen; I hope Sister forgets to hang up our papers today.

It's lunchtime. We eat at our desk. There is room for two but no one wants to be my partner; I don't have a plaid lunch box. I open my grocery-size brown bag containing a baked-bean sandwich and a homemade cookie, wrapped in wax paper. Sister Mary Elizabeth pushes the candy and juice cart into our classroom. The girls with plaid lunch boxes buy Three Musketeers and orange juice in little bottles. Those of us with baked-bean sandwiches in brown bags quench our thirst at the water fountain. I wish Sister Mary Elizabeth would move her cart. I need to see if anything is being dropped into the Poor Box. I hate kids who don't eat their lunch. The cold bean sandwich sticks in my throat as I think about the afternoon reading lesson.

One o'clock! "Mary Nicholls, stand and read paragraph three," says Sister. Why must we stand and read? I'm sure my mouth would obey my brain if I could sit instead and I could use a piece of paper to help me separate the words and lines. Oh God, oh God, my words are spilling out like a laundry bag full of dirty socks; nothing making sense. I hate kids who giggle.

It's that time again, ten of three. God, be merciful and let me die now! Even with my eyes closed I can smell the unwanted lunches being dumped into the big brown paper-bag by the smartest boy in the class, David Roberts. He gives the bag to Sister Loretta. I feel sick. I hate kids who don't eat their lunch. God, can I at least faint? "Mary Nicholls," Sister calls, as I knew she would. It is a hundred miles to the front of the classroom. I feel the piercing eyes of all seventy-two kids and the whispers of Brenda, Mildred, and Lois. As though I am naked, I stand before the class as Sister hands me the Poor Box. She has a soft smile; she asks about my mother, sends her love to my sisters and brother, and reminds me that God loves me. I hate kids who whisper, I hate kids who don't eat their lunch, and I hate rain! I want to hate sister but it's not allowed. God, forgive her, she knows not what she does.

<hr />

The Innocence of Ignorance

I.
Fresh and alive with no one to teach her, nothing to warn her, except experience—as she gains it. Innocent Eve, with no folklore stories passed along for
her to ponder, and pass her time. How long the purity of day must seem—
with no dream of past participations, or scary apprehensions, poor thing.
And no clothes yet, to make, or wear—no wash, no ironing, no sorting
through seasonal woes.

II.
Let's face it, Eve had little else to do but obsess over all things not hers, poor
thing, new to verdant life and she, no angel, a fertile crescent away from city
lures and cures, unknowingly puts up with no cold cellar prepared to store
excess(eve) energy.

III.
No meals to cook either, no smoke, no fire, no wizened mid-wife there to
warn her.
The facts of life remain, yes, they remain un-preached, unplanned,
un-plotted too.

IV.
Look around, no kitchen develops cunning capture plans, no poison-apple
recipes to make, or follow, no friends to share the innocent boredom of Eden
innocence.

V.
Except (A)dam man, and he, poor thing, with no March
Madness distraction and no cold shower to douse roused
passion—fruit-of-the-spirit-side-tracked—
he's busy pruning trees of knowledge; grafting forbidden-apple branches
onto the only pair in the garden, poor things.

VI.
Look again, no books to read, or write, no serpent dissertation explanations, for that matter, no scrubbings down, no grinding halts, or off-course faults to body scan, only restless thumbs to twiddle and idle hands ripe for picking-up life's problems.

VII.
Undisciplined, yet determined, with their destiny inbred, these two private beings invent—and pass along- a made-up-game of guilt & blame & shame, victim-perpetrator-style, poor things, newly arrived in a state of grace, not ever Eve(n) lost....

Ruth M. Alcorn

I Remember

Mimi S. Dupont

I remember being stunned by things my children said. Stunned enough for what they said to give me pause, to stay with me throughout my life and guide me. Sometimes those pronouncements gave others pause, because I shared what my children said and, sometimes, others heard the wisdom, too.

I remember the morning I got three children off to school, packed up the fourth child's bag and what I needed for work, then loaded the car, buckled her into her car seat and shut the back door, climbed into the driver's seat, buckled myself in and started the car. I remember she was three, not yet toilet trained, still using a pacifier which she would spit out occasionally to make her pronouncements in complex sentences. Apparently her brain developed ahead of her bladder.

I remember saying "uh, huh" as all parents do when we're listening with only part of ourselves and the other part is concentrating on getting the immediate things taken care of: starting the car, mentally checking that we've put everything needed for the day into the car, shifting into the correct gear, then looking outside the car for the first time to assess what's happening there.

I don't remember the weather or the time of year. But I do remember that her tone of voice told me she was clearly irritated I was not giving her my full attention. Finally she'd had enough. I had just buckled up and started the car and I remember when she said: "Weren't you listening to what you heard?" I raised a finger to correct her—because surely she meant "Weren't you listening to what I said"—when my every movement stopped. I didn't move the car. I didn't move my limbs. I didn't move my mouth. Because I realized she meant exactly what she'd said. Yes, I'd heard her. No, I wasn't listening to what I'd heard—to what she said.

I've shared that incident with college students in classes on critical reading and thinking, with company employees in seminars on communication, with welfare recipients preparing to get a job, with colleagues examining better ways to relate as we get our work done individually and in teams. So I'm not the only one who has come to appreciate that we often do not listen to what we hear.

Ears are made to hear. They pick up sound waves. They send the sound waves to the brain. The brain decodes. We hear. Remember? Remember hearing your mother's voice? Remember hearing the ocean for the first time? Remember a friend whispering in your ear? Remember hearing the exuberant roar when the home team scored? I remember hearing many sounds that deeply influenced my life.

I remember hearing the swish as the ocean washed onto the beach, back out, and back in again the first time my parents took us to the beach. And I thought, with wonder, this goes on forever. Tide in. Tide out. Twice a day. Every day. Forever. I remember feeling very small looking out at that vast ocean and knowing—because I was good at geography—that Europe and Africa were beyond the horizon on the other side. I felt small, and insignificant, but not unimportant. I marveled then at that paradox. I was thrilled to be standing at the edge of a continent. Still am. All that from hearing the swish of the Atlantic Ocean waves.

Unless there is a storm, the sound of the waves is pretty soft. It stays in the background, not interfering with a conversation held in our beach chairs or as we bob up and down just beyond the breakers on a sparkling day, at the edge of the continent.

Many of life's most precious sounds are soft and small: the far-off hoot of an owl, the rustle of wind through the pine forest, a baby breathing in sleep. So if I can hear—and appreciate—those sounds every day, why do I not always listen to what I hear when someone is speaking to me?

Well, partly it's that human communication is complicated. Do we always say what we mean? Do we always mean what we say? Can I trust what you're saying if your tone of voice tells me something else? Screaming at me that you're NOT ANGRY is not convincing.

Then there is that word "always." I try never to use absolutes. See? It's hard! So I'm just going to work at improving my percentages, like a baseball player working to improve his batting average. Maybe listening more intentionally to the soft, small sounds in life will help me listen better to the people in my life.

———~~~~~ ✳ ~~~~~———

my child

how do you bind the wounds
of your child
who is already grown

the slings and arrows
of the adult world
launched and found a home

whipped by a tide
of circumstance
defeated on many sides

the smile that once
lit up my life
hidden now deep inside

this life i gave
in overwhelming love
protected as hard as i knew

got down on my knees
to absorb the pain
help him get well and grow

held his hand
to steady his path
guided him until he could fly

please show me how
to bind his wounds now
dear god, at least let me try

jahill

---

*

kia

the bugle blows its mournful sound
in sunshine rain or snow

a flag is draped upon a box
someone's child lies still below

one more counted is now dead
fighting in a far-off land

sent by someone safe at home
as bullets fly into the sand

lovers mothers fathers kids
crumble in despair

cry out in their misery
how can this be fair

whose proud flag rests on the box
matters little on this day

the one they loved is now dead
what else is there to say

centuries have taught us little
about the hell of war

we send them off with bands
with cheers speeches much applause

when they pay the final price
we honor them in poem

do we really understand
they are never coming home

our creator bows his head in shame
we fight we kill then use his name

he made us in his image
to love to get along

how many more must die
will we ever learn

jahill

Falsification

Judy Wood

They bob above the waves, two small white foam bra cups floating away
from us. My mom and I are laughing so hard we can barely keep our heads
out of the water. A few weeks ago, Mom purchased a new suit for this year's
beach vacation and if it hadn't been for the padded inserts everything would
have been okay.

Our family has come for our annual two-week summer vacation in
Rehoboth. I suffered through the ride here sandwiched between my two
younger brothers in the way back of our SUV. In the middle seat rode the
twins, two years old this summer, and our nanny, Marianne. My Dad drove
and my mom shadow drove. That part is so annoying. She lurches from
side to side and slams her foot to the floor as if she has a brake on her side. I
couldn't see from my position in the rear of the car today, but it's what she
always does. Plus, I could hear my dad asking her if she wanted to drive and
my mom laughing and saying she thought she was driving.

We rent the same house every summer. Our house is about a block off
the beach with a big wrap-around porch and a hammock in the yard. The
best part of our rental is that it's big enough so I can have my own room. We
wear our swim suits for the ride and pack a cooler full of drinks and snacks
so the minute we unload we're ready to head for the beach.

Today we're lucky. Our early departure from home, which had produced much groaning and yet another argument between Mom and me,
has allowed us to arrive in time to avoid the crowds and find a perfect spot
to settle. Dad rocked the umbrella back and forth until it lodged deep in
the sand and then he challenged Mikey and Sam to a race to the water.
Marianne managed to get the twins happily playing with their pails and
shovels. And that left Mom and me.

I'll admit this year has been tough. I'm not sure why I'm always feeling
so irritable with my family, especially my mom. My mother's actually pretty
cool; in fact, my friends all love her. Maybe it's because she likes to tease me
and I rarely think she's funny; like when she pretends to be me and goes
around the house sighing, stomping her feet, and slamming doors and making dramatic gestures with her arms while crying, "I'm so misunderstood. I
don't belong in this family. I 'vant' to be alone." When I complain, she just

smiles and pats me on the head and tells me she's trying to teach me to see the humor in things.

Today is a hot August day and already the humidity has my hair sticking to the back of my neck.

"Should we swim or walk first?" Mom asks.

"Definitely swim," I say.

We head for the ocean. Mom strides out into the water and I follow. Battling the undertow and staying on top of the waves, we swim side by side until we are about fifty yards from shore.

When we stop to rest, I can spot my dad and my brothers roughhousing and running in and out of the water. The lifeguards are perched on the tall white lifeguard stands and their red swimsuits make them stand out even from far away. The beach is filling up and, from this distance, it's looks like a patchwork quilt covered with constantly changing patterns. I turn away from the shore just in time to see an enormous wave building and rolling in fast toward mom and me. I yell to my mother to watch out and we both dive. I'm under for what seems like forever before I manage to get my head up over the top. I see Mom sputtering and spitting out water as she lifts her head up over a wave. That's when we both notice the bra cups. There they are bobbing up and down like we are. Both of us start to laugh at the same time. Our giggles expand until we are flailing our arms and sinking and emerging like buoys.

I swallow a big gulp of water as I try to catch onto them. That's when I notice that the lifeguards have abandoned their chairs, grabbed their gear and are heading out into the ocean. Mom sees them at the same time and says, "Uh oh. I wonder who's in trouble. They're heading out fast." We both scan the water to see if we can locate who's in danger. Neither of us pick up on anyone who might be in need of being saved. But the lifeguards keep swimming. We notice that almost everyone on the beach has stopped what they're doing and are watching what's happening in the water.

Mom says, "Liz, I think they're heading for us."

I realize she's right and scream, "Oh my God. They are. They're going to rescue us. This is a nightmare. We aren't drowning. Mom, do something. At least get your falsies. Hurry. Oh my God."

Mom makes a few stabs at trying to scoop up the offending bra cups, but between the waves and her hiccups from her laughter jostling her movements, she can never quite reach them. Before we know it, two lifeguards are next to us and handing us ropes attached to ring buoys. I try to tell them that we're okay, that we aren't drowning, that we don't need their help, but they ignore me and insist that we grab onto the ropes and let them pull us to shore. One of the guards spots the falsies drifting away. "What are those?" he says.

I say, "Oh don't worry about those. They're nothing. Tissues maybe. Jelly fish? Let's just go."

For once Mom doesn't contradict me or make a joke and I'm relieved. Being pulled into shore is enough of an embarrassment. We get to where our feet touch and the lifeguards let us go. A group of people on the beach breaks into cheers and applauds the lifeguards for saving the day. Mom stops and waves to the crowd and I hear her telling them a cheery thank you as I dart for our blanket.

Throwing myself face down onto the blanket, I vow that I will never come to Rehoboth again. Maybe next year I can talk my parents into a vacation in Fiji or some other distant place where I will be comfortable showing my face. Meanwhile my mom comes back to the blanket, slips down beside me and says, "Well, that was quite an experience. All this time coming to Rehoboth and I don't think I've ever been saved before. Weren't those lifeguards cute? Wasn't the blond the one you had a crush on last year? Are you hungry? I'm going to have a sandwich. Want one?"

Is she kidding? No I don't want a sandwich. Instead I want to find a way to disappear. I try to bury myself deeper into the blanket when Dad and my brothers come running back to our umbrella followed by Marianne and the twins.

Mikey says, "Wow that was so cool. Were you guys really scared? Did you think you were gonna die? The lifeguards were totally amazing. Everyone on the beach was watching." Just as I'm about to tell him he's an idiot and of course we weren't drowning, my Dad reaches down and pulls my mom up in a bear hug and plants kisses all over her face. This is a new humiliation that I am just beginning to contend with when I glimpse something happening at the lifeguard chair. Three boys are bringing something over to the stand followed by a small crowd. I prop myself up on my elbows to get a better look. The boys exchange some conversation with the guards at which point one of the guards blows a whistle and holds up whatever the boys brought him. I squint but I can't make out what he's holding. Sam races for the stand and I wait for him to come back and tell us what's happening.

When he returns, he tells us that they've got some kind of small spongy things. He says he doesn't know what they are but they look boring. Before

I can consider what this means, my mother screams with delight, "Isn't that wild? I bet someone's rescued the pads for my bathing suit."

I leap to my feet as if the sand is on fire and grab her by the shoulders. "Mom, you can't seriously be thinking that you're going to go over and get them."

"Lizzy, of course I am. This is a brand new bathing suit and I was sorry to lose them. And, if you stop and think about it for a minute, it's really funny."

I am beside myself with horror as I say, "Mom, if you do that honestly I will never speak to you again."

With a grin and a pat to my head, she marches over to collect her falsies from the lifeguards.

Much, much later in my life I am sitting in a white dress next to the man I've sworn to love forever. That man just happened to be one of the boys that was on the beach that day. My dad stands to give a toast and this very story is the one he chooses to tell. Life is funny if you let it be.

———————✳———————

Homily to Spring

gather strength to seeds
they bud
warmed in new light
soon to bloom and root

how to stay and be kind
on frosty morning
how to thrill a storm
of sunlight

slow and away slip
the winter doesits dust weakened my sight
and spun wind frombare branches

pinched my softened heart here
let lowered some weight.
this thrust of your cusp
need not turn from me
to sigh

wounds worst like the first
birth of green
burst of life
raining and rising

what if a hollow bud?

that shining stream doctors
this sober church of thought
contained within a metal vessel
but pouring for your prodding

to submit I am loose, kissed,
and sunken under the weather

welcome dawn
bless our sins of night
cradle this bud
warmed is cracking open
and inside a hue of light.

Irene Emily Wanberg

———————✳———————

Riel's Tower

Terri Clifton

Riel admitted to herself that she was dying. The knowledge had come to her gradually, like the shortness of her breath, this weakness that stole upon her each time she climbed these stairs. She stopped for a long moment, hand resting on the cold metal rail, before ascending to the top.

She'd never leave this tower, never escape the wasteland. It was hard to accept. All this time she'd believed she'd eventually go home. It was the dream that had kept her sane over the decades of confinement. The simple trust that somehow the Commonwealth would be defeated and she would be freed. On the worst days, when she'd been lonely or afraid, she'd replayed in her head the smell of green grass, the sound of water gurgling in the little creek beside her house. Now the images tore at her weakening heart.

She looked down at her hands, at the bluish tinge beneath her nails, and an old anger welled up inside her. How many years have I lost, she wondered. Perhaps she should have marked the days, but she hadn't, and now there was no way of knowing. One day had been the same as every other among the red-orange dirt and rock. There was only day and night, hot and cold.

She touched a silver button and one half of the rounded wall slid inside the other. Her world view was a semicircle. The dry, heated air enveloped her as she stepped forward. The sun had slipped away only moments ago, behind far distant mountains now etched sharp against a sky rapidly changing from flame-orange to water-blue.

This was her ritual. Waiting away the day's blistering glare of high desert sun, emerging from the tower as the first stars were becoming visible, their glow the softest silver in the new night. It was beautiful, and was still the only thing that soothed her.

In the beginning she had raged, running up and down the five stories of her prison, looking for a door or a window, finding none. It had taken weeks before she'd discovered the moving wall that allowed her access to the outside. She'd learned that night time was the only reasonable time for such outings. Now as she settled on a cushion she forced her breathing to come deep and slow. The sky above slipped into full darkness and the starlight hardened to piercing brilliance. She let her mind drift beyond her prescribed world.

Behind her, the stairs clanged softly. Like clockwork, as expected. Riel realized this pattern would come to an end. How soon?

"Hello, Ace," she said, without turning.

Ace put the tray of watermint tea between them, then took its place on the opposite pillow. Riel insisted on the use of the cushion, although the android didn't feel the same aches in its body as she did. She looked at its humanish face. Time would never touch it.

"You look exactly the same as you always have, while I believe I have gotten old." She pulled her braid forward over her shoulder. It reached her knees, thick and grey. No hint of her chestnut curls.

Ace's head tilted. Riel knew the android was processing, its artificial intelligence buzzing away. Oh how she'd hated the evil machine in the early days, screaming at it while it maintained inhuman patience. She'd even refused the food that it offered her, until she'd fainted and been forced to realize that to ever get out she'd need to stay alive. It hurt now, remembering the willful optimism. Maybe if she'd known how many years would pass by she would have let the life and fight drain from her.

Ace's strange eyes had been the first thing she'd seen when she'd regained consciousness. "I am adaptive artificial intelligence," came the voice. "I am programmed to serve you in your quarantine. Your infection must not endanger other humans. I am to simulate humanity as well as serve your physical needs."

"Simulate humanity?" Laughter had half choked her and she coughed the hysteria away. "And to prevent my escape."

"This tower is your life support. You will not survive outside of it."

The truth of it had burned her. Even if she gained a way out, it meant crossing terrain that was deadly, with no idea of which direction to go.

Even after all this time the memories still caused hurt, and the pain beneath Riel's sternum began to blossom. She rose, stretched her arms over her head, hoping to ease it.

Ace hummed away, the only sound in the world.

She walked in small circles, but the pressure inside didn't abate. Her memories pursued her relentlessly.

Her books, her writings, had been taken, but she'd still had a mind and a voice. After discovering this rooftop she'd climbed up to talk to the stars every night, sending her words into the sky. Ace had followed her, of course.

Night after night she'd woven stories or recited her poems to the heavens. Ace always next to her, never saying a word until one night when Riel had wished out loud that she could remember the poem from the night before. Ace had repeated it verbatim, mimicking Riel's inflections and cadences perfectly.

68

Riel had been overcome with a tangle of emotions she couldn't sort. Picking at the tangle she'd grasped that she had an Auxiliator Class Enhanced companion with a perfect memory. What a sense of rebellion and mutiny had come upon her when she'd understood there was a way to keep creating. She had laughed out loud and danced about the rooftop, singing silly songs and having Ace play them back, over and over. She would find a way to take Ace with her once she was free and she'd have a body of work waiting to replace what had been destroyed.

Since that night she had invented every kind of story, had given her imagination unlimited reign, but tonight the only story she wanted to tell was her own.

As she paced, she did just that.

Her life had been normal enough, and if she'd been shy and awkward, it hadn't mattered much. Her parents loved their only child, and never peered too closely at the scribbling she did in her little diaries, and Riel never even thought of sharing her written daydreams with anyone. She knew it was odd, so she'd kept it all to herself. Until the day she'd met a boy who smiled at her, and they had walked through the old orchard with apple blossoms falling. It had felt like she could tell him anything. Eventually she showed him a poem she'd written, and he'd asked to keep it, not knowing they were setting chaos into motion.

Men had come to her house, battering open the door. They had struck her father. Her mother stood stiff and pale as death as Riel's room was searched. Her books were seized. Riel was arrested. It was the last she'd seen of any of them.

She spent the next months in a reform school for troubled youth. She watched the process work on the minds of her peers and it began to scare her, so she did the only thing she knew how to do. She invented stories about the people around her, refining them inside her mind in the dark hours when nightmares shook her awake.

Hearing a new girl crying in the dark after one horrible dream, something inside Riel threatened to come unwound at the sound. She had to stop it, so she'd crept to the girl's bed, silent on bare feet.

Small and fragile looking, the girl couldn't have been more than eleven or twelve, curled in a fetal position, head to the wall. For the first time in many months, Riel felt more than anger. She had soothed the girl but Riel knew someone so fragile would be quickly broken. Still, she tried to be her friend, and the nights when the crying haunted her, Riel would sit next to her and tell her stories.

She never knew how it was found out, just that one morning there were two guards at the end of her bed.

There had been no trial when she was brought to judgment. Her head had already been shaved and she had been forced to wear clothes of unbleached cloth without adornment. The clothing of a penitent. They told her she was a criminal. She wanted to shout she was guilty of nothing, but seven sets of cold eyes stole her voice.

"You are guilty of corruptive untruths. The creation of such lies poses grave danger to all. In a society of truth there is no place for fiction. History teaches us that your kind simply cannot be redeemed. You will not be allowed to infect others."

Fear razed through Riel. Against her will she shuddered, but forced herself to keep her head up. She searched out the cruelest face, the woman in the middle. A hood covered her hair but Riel guessed it was the same steel as her irises.

"You would kill me then?"

The woman sneered and folded her hands on the black table, at ease in her zealotry. "Life is sacred. Because we believe this, yours will be spared. You are hereby sentenced to humane quarantine." She smiled.

Hands seized Riel, and she struggled against them, still looking at the semi-circle of judges, wondering what that meant. The small pssh of the injection gun caused her head to turn. In a slow motion reaction, she felt the sting in her arm and had only enough time to think they had lied and that they were killing her, before everything faded to black.

"I was surprised to wake up at all," she said, as much to herself as to Ace. The stars moved in their same paths, the great swath of galaxies burned above. Looking up, she still tried to believe in her place in it all, even as she was dying in vain.

She went back to her story, as if Ace hadn't been there for the rest of it. She poured out all of the things she'd felt, just needing to lift them from her heart. All that she'd thought, and feared, and lost.

When the sun rose, she retreated inside and to bed, but her body proved as restless as her spirit. She didn't want to waste hours sleeping.

Every floor of the windowless structure had huge monitors, floor to ceiling vistas of forests, lakes, mountains—whatever one chose. Riel had asked for them to be turned off soon after she'd arrived. Now their empty grayness was haunting her. She sought out Ace to turn them back on.

The inside of the elevator tube had always been like a tightening of the already constricting prison. It unnerved her, so she used the stairs, finding the breathlessness involved with dozens of steps and the pressure in her chest still to be preferable to the trapped sensation.

Ace was on the bottom level tending the food sources that allowed the tower to be completely isolated. Normally the robot was busily moving about, checking the systems that produced fish, snails, mushrooms, berries and greens. This day, Riel found it with hands poised above the micro greens, clippers ready, but paused. She watched a moment, having the oddest sense of catching Ace daydreaming.

Screens reactivated, Riel was sorry she had waited so long. Still unable to sleep, she rested while watching the natural vistas. It fascinated her that she was almost able to feel the prickle of catching snowflakes on her tongue, or the tug of tiny waves on a tropical beach. With her routine broken, it was fully dark before she sought out the roof top.

She did not begin a story as Ace sat beside her. Instead, she asked questions.

"What do you know about dying, Ace?"

"There is a protocol." Ace whirred and clicked but offered nothing more.

"Will someone come?" She tried to imagine another human here.

"A drone will return and retrieve the cargo."

The thought of her body as cargo was chilling. She wasn't sure if she wanted to know any more.

"What will happen to you?"

"I don't know."

Riel was surprised to find that she harbored affection for the machine. They sat in silence for a long time until another disturbing thought occurred to Riel. Her stories would no doubt be erased from the hard drive, as if they had never been. When she'd asked Ace if that would happen, Ace was silent, then the whirring sped up.

"Ace?"

"It can be assumed that my system will be shut down."

Riel's thoughts raced wildly. It was more than she could bear that she would die, that Ace would essentially die, that her stories would die.

"We have to find a way for you to escape. I'll help you. If you get away before they can deprogram you, you could take my stories. I could die with peace that way, if I thought there was a chance that other people could hear them, and think."

If a robot could look wistful, Ace did. The lift of its head, the stare into the distant dark. Riel would have sworn it was imagination inside the carbon fiber skull.

"Please, Ace?"

Once it had been decided there was still the task of figuring out how to do it. They had discussed options through the night, dismissing notions of building a parachute or a glider. Riel was near exhaustion when she reached her bed.

She slept the whole day, not stirring once, and woke to Ace sitting patiently next to her.

"I think I know how it could be done," it said.

The solution was inelegant. Anchored on the roof, the cables from the elevator dropped over the edge.

Riel peered down, still able to see the ground in the fading light. "It doesn't reach!"

"It is not necessary. I have calculated the impact and it should cause no damage to hardware or software."

Riel felt very old and mortal. Her bones could never withstand such a drop. Nor could she ever survive crossing the hellish terrain. Her heart squeezed, but it was a much different sort of pain. She would miss her companion. Machine that it was, it was still her only friend. She pondered saying something meaningful, of prolonging the time left, but knew it would serve no purpose. Only letting go would achieve anything now. "I suppose there's no reason to wait, Ace?"

"No reason," it said.

Riel watched the downward climb, winced as Ace let go and fell. Her heart nearly stopped in the long seconds before she saw movement.

"Good luck, Ace!" She waved, holding her other hand to her chest.

A pale blue beam lit Riel's face and she laughed. Then the light was gone, and Ace with it.

She talked to the stars again that night, a story about an unusual friendship, and the stars listened. Brilliance, they said. Brilliance.

She was all alone now, in her final chapter, and surprised to find it didn't scare her. Freedom, she thought, must sometimes be only on the inside. The mind. The heart. "However long mine keeps beating," she said. "This is *my* tower and here I am free."

～～～～＊～～～～

My Poem to Self

She unto me / I unto her
So in honor / today I will embrace her
Me / We / Yes / something similar to the trinity
My mother / nature / making me this natural nurturer of all things
Today I embrace gentle winds blown of butterfly wing echoes /
kind of heart in me
Embrace the strong tower / root solid in ground oak standing tall /
spine of me
Yes / natural nurturer in me
Embrace hands small / as seeds planted deep
This touch blooms of humanity reach your core/ and conjures
all you will live for
Venture they dare / to the depths of me
Embrace my attempts to ensure none drown embrace ability
of transparency to cleanse them
Yes / me / womb of alchemy
Concocts fragrance you long never intend to become consumed in
How dare you
My mother / nature / life's care taker and I / life giver
Yes / me
Embrace the silent sounds inside breaths air heir to spirits throne
Sitting high in order to embrace it all
Each vibration / hearts beat rhythm echoes and creates profound sound
Embrace tears formed in the wells of me
To my virginity / I'm sorry
Yes / me
Today I embrace me
Muddy creek your water became
So many sturdy appearing weak levy / wood rotted kind of men
And Me In tune to this river's flow / flowed
Today I embrace forgiving me
Yes / me
Similar to the trinity
Mother / nature / me

The sacrifice revived of loves spirit
Forgiving me
Two beings alive of me / one still abides in me
Yes / me
Once a murderer to life attempting to escape me
Embrace my sorrows
Gray clouds simply part because / you sunshine
Remain hidden in clouds / where rainfall kind of tears weep
from heaven's skies
Today I embrace / me
Autumn leaves falling kind of brown
Caught up in my mother's rapture time enough not to touch ground /
withered dead
Yet close enough to know dead / and embrace her winds
refreshing of being born again
Yes / me "Tha Rebirth" of all things plain but beautiful
Pure / but lived
Funny / but pained
Innocent / but wise
Transparent / but scared
Loved / but alone
Eternal / but carnal
Sensitive / but courageous
Yes / me
Unto her / she unto me
So I honor
Today I will embrace her / me / we
Yes / something similar to the trinity
My mother / nature making me this natural nurturer of all things
Including / embracing me.

Ash'iz "Tha Rebirth"

———~~~~~✳~~~~~———

What We Keep

In the restless Spring of my twenties,
Mom boarded an overnight train bound
for my latest address, resolved to help
me settle. She tossed off her mules, puffed
on her Pall Malls, and got to work.
Mom knew how to keep house: sprayed
each room with Lysol, scrubbed floors,
shopped at the local five-and-dime
for a wind chime strung with sea shells,
a welcome mat branded with a pelican,
placed them at my front door. Mom was tired
of tracking my moves, tired of replacing
each entry in her book with new cities,
zip codes, tired of trying to ground my shaky roots.
After weeks of wear, we called a truce,
perhaps lulled by the sun's insistent warmth,
the Gulf's hypnotic pull. We linked arms,
curled our toes in the forgiving sand,
the daughter who strayed, the mother who stayed
inside firm, familiar borders. After she died
that winter, this is what I kept: a snapshot,
unlike all others—Mom, her salon-proof hair
unbound, whipped by the wind, an enduring
smile framed by untouched lips, all this, all this,
under a wide and bountiful sky.

Irene Fick

This poem was first published in the Mojave River Review in 2014

❋

Being Love

Who am I to know so well
my love, to feel its flash
burst through
each breathing pore, hold
its throbbing ache, a molten beat
trapped deep within my heart
—no, deeper still—
within my churning core?

Who am I to look to love to feed
my certain crave
and bleed my longing sighs, then
satisfy my empty being with promise
kept beyond
my glutton dreams?

Who am I?

Answer love,
with blessed
love,
...and know.

Ruth M. Alcorn

The Wedding Dress

Ginny Daly

The time: Summer 1961—my sister Mary had just become engaged.
The place: Washington, D.C.

The protagonist: John Jay Daly, Washington Post
drama critic and father to five daughters all named
"Mary Something" after my mother Mary.

This particular evening Daddy leaves the bar of the National Press Club
at 14th and F Streets, N.W. On the opposite corner: Washington's iconic
department store, Julius Garfinkel's. Daddy loved Garfinkel's!
    Something in Garfinkel's curved corner two-story high window catches
Daddy's eye. There it is. Empire style, scoop neck, nipped waist, long sleeves,
silk shantung, Belgian lace at the neck and wrists, 77 bride's buttons
A classically elegant wedding dress.

Not just any dress. The Dress.

Now my father was an Irish romantic, never a practical man. Mom, the
Midwest banker's daughter, was the realistic one. Overcome by a burst of
unusual practicality, Daddy rides up to Garfinkel's 6th floor bridal department and buys the dress.

Rationale: One daughter getting married, four to go, they need a dress. And
here's a beautiful one. Yes, a wedding dress is just a darn good thing to have
on hand, much like a lawn mower, a snow shovel or jumper cables. There
when you need it, at the ready. Only thing required was a fitting. Seemed
logical.

Imagine the hue and cry at our house that night!
Jack, you did what????

My sister Mary wore The Dress for her wedding. As did other brides. Many others. And not just sisters. Nieces. Cousins. Friends. Friends of friends. Remember, it only needs a fitting. Cleaning and storage, natch. Perhaps an alteration, some taking in or letting out...maybe a bit of replacement fabric. Last worn 2006. The Dress now has a library card of its appearances which stays with it in storage.

The price? $99
The legacy? Priceless

Maybe Daddy wasn't so crazy after all.

------------*------------

What I Will Whisper in My Son's Ear While We Dance

Mimi S. Dupont

It was Monday morning. My son was getting married—Saturday—and I had a 700-word assignment due—that afternoon—for the last session of my first ever writers workshop. My mind was on the wedding.

I have three daughters, two of whom had already walked the excruciating-but-eventually-rewarding path of wedding-planning-then-execution, making me two-thirds of an expert on being mother of the bride. But I have only one son, and thus had zero experience at being mother of the groom. By the Monday before the wedding I could tell you with 100% certainty that this Venn diagram of wedding mother experiences had, max, 2% overlap. I knew very little about the upcoming nuptials except that I loved my son; loved his almost-bride; would probably deeply enjoy every aspect of the wedding weekend; oh, and I knew what song he and I would dance to at the reception because I'd had to pick it the previous week.

I had been working for several weeks on reprinting some old and not-so-old photos and encasing them all in an eclectic but themed group of frames for display at the rehearsal dinner. My gaze kept wandering from the blank page on the laptop screen waiting for me to record the next Nobel Prize-winning piece of literature to the pile of photos and frames on my rough wooden table.

I tenderly fingered the images of my son as a child in old photos, curled up after being wrested away from the sticky baby album pages, and recalled his blonde bowl cut as a toddler, his first school picture—kindergarten—in which he sported the new glasses that made him look like Harry Potter—before Harry Potter ever was, and a Little League photo showing one of the pitches that made him an occasional closer in addition to short stop.

I remembered, when he was three, how he wore the yellow plastic top to the hot air popcorn popper on his head like a super-hero helmet.

I remembered, when he was six, how he cried every day before he went to school in first grade, little book bag strapped to his little body, legs straight out across the sofa cushion while he waited for the bus. Never a man of many words, it was November before he finally said why he was crying.

I remembered the Little League and school ball games in which he pitched, caught, fielded, batted, ran and sometimes stole his way home. Occasionally he was put in as the closer. In characteristic modesty, he always said he was good for one inning—until they figured out his pitches.

I remembered that I was going to dance with him on Saturday at his wedding reception, probably the only time in his life and mine we would ever dance together. And then I knew what I wanted to tell him, so I wrote it down—and took it to my writing workshop. My colleagues encouraged me to give it to my son, so I printed it on textured paper, attached photos that matched the memories, framed it and took it with me when I left for Baltimore, Maryland.

I took it to the rehearsal dinner and set it up with all the framed photos, but never had the chance to give it to him. I took it to the wedding, but never had an opportunity there either to present it to him. So I took it to the Sunday brunch and, arriving early, placed the photos all around on the tables still bedecked with bouquets of antique roses. His framed gift I put on the buffet table leaning against a two-foot pedestal with an enormous arrangement of roses atop it.

As I prepared to leave, I asked him if he had seen it yet and he said, yes, he'd seen it but not read it yet. So I retrieved it from its place of honor. As I handed it to him, I said I didn't expect to see it hanging on their living room wall the next time I visited. But I smiled, and suggested he hang it in his clothes closet so he would see it every morning when he arms himself with suit and tie for his daily workplace warfare. Then he can remember how very much he is loved.

What I Will Whisper in My Son's Ear While We Dance

What will I whisper in my son's ear
while we dance at his wedding?

I will tell him
that while I have not always been the perfect mother,
he has always been the perfect son,
the son I longed for
the son I dreamed of
the son I loved from before he was conceived of
and before he was conceived.

I will tell him
he was so welcome when he came into the world
that someone I knew planted a huge stork in our front yard
that said Welcome Home Timothy Richard 8lb 5oz
and his father took a picture next to the sign
of me holding all eight pounds and six ounces of him
(I'm sure it was six ounces)
wrapped in a spare cotton blanket because it was almost summer
and his two older sisters were smiling and squinting into the sun.
And then I took a picture next to the sign
of his father holding the little bundle of Tim
while his sister Kate leaned casually against the sign
and his sister Betsy kissed his bald little hours-old head.

I will tell him
that yes, yes I did come to most of his games
even though he doesn't remember it
because I remember filling out forms to take vacation time
so I could leave work early enough to get to an after school game.

I will tell him
that sometimes a parent can't be your friend
like when I made him substitute a course because he wanted to drop Spanish
and taking accounting turned out to be
the turn in his coursework that started his business career,
although I don't pretend to take credit for that,
just for having tough love when it was called for.

I will tell him
I'm not sorry for the tough love times
or the times I bugged him until he gave me an answer,
not because I enjoyed irritating him, quite the opposite,
but because I wanted to help him out of his pain
or help him decide
or help him not decide and keep his options open.

I will tell him then
that I loved him from the start,
and I will love him til the end.

By then Nat King Cole will have stopped singing Unforgettable
and we will have stopped dancing
and I will whisper:
I will never stop loving you, Son.
I will love you always,
but I can share you
because there is enough love to go around.

<center>~~~~~~*~~~~~~</center>

Blue Island

They parted on a day when rain dampened
her new denim dress. This was not the razzle
dazzle of a summer shower, jeweling the hibiscus,
but rather a filmy gray lackadaisical rain, like one
captured in an old photo where the landscape
is blurred and one lone drop stains the foreground.
In the distance a train moaned its warning, and
the scent of diesel annoyed the air. He offered
what he imagined was a condolence: a Swiss
knife equipped with tools for reassembling her life
without him. She used it instead to slash the satin
ribbons that once bound the first bouquet of wild
daisies he gave her, then hung the tattered ribbons
from her rearview mirror like a piece of salvaged art.

Gail Braune Comorat

~~~~~~~~~~~*~~~~~~~~~~~

Finding Home

Kimberly Blanch

My eyes floated open. The strands of sunlight coming through the skylight hinted at warmth in the air on this seemingly brisk May morning in Maine. The bed called out to me, stay, but the impetus to initiate what *would be* was stronger than the familiarity of *what was*.

Today was the day.

It all began so beautifully, so romantically. We'd languished in that delicious, lustful phase of a love. A new love. How incredible it had been. Months together. Months apart. Anticipation building as the next meeting time would near. The chemistry undeniable. How silly to believe for a second that it wouldn't engulf us.

But something had happened. A lot happened, as a matter of fact. Oh, facts. What insidious things. They certainly wound their way into our existence. *Fact* had led me to my decision on this particular morning. The growing lack of love, trust and respect that began as a crack evolved into a chasm. An earthly cut too deep and too wide to cross anymore. I on one side and he on the other.

In preparation, I consciously opted for comfort. The soft plush of my most comfortable pants, the caress of my favorite cashmere sweater. Sweet, soft armor to declare my decision. Navigating my way through the carnage of his scattered clothing, I exited our bedroom knowing that "our" didn't truly exist in this space.

Each carpeted step rose to meet my next footfall, as if it were supporting me before I descended to the next. Entering what had become his office, the windowed one of course, I felt drawn to perch myself upon the corner of the rosewood piano bench, as if to embody the notion of flight.

The early May sunshine struck the unkempt piles on his desk, and hints of light peeked through his disheveled mahogany curls. Robust French roast brewed in the kitchen and wafted in from around the corner. Amazing how just the aroma can enliven the mind.

I knew what I needed to do. "I'm done," I said.

"Done with what, the coffee?"

"With us," I said. "Done with us."

"What do you mean?" He turned toward me with a furrowed brow and that stockade of a beard. Through the years, it seemed the thickness of his beard always symbolized the distance he desired between us. He wore it like a shield, to defend himself against any inkling of intimacy.

It must have been the calmness in my steadfast stare that made him take notice. This time. I had threatened this before but could never follow through. It always felt as if I would lose a limb by leaving him…so I would find myself back-diving into our pool of dysfunction yet again. But this was different.

His quizzical look tugged at the remaining string hanging from my heart. To stand strong in my conviction, I quickly recalled some clips from our more recent reels. The trip we took to Chile with friends, when an unapproved word or deed from me resulted in total silence from him. Or the trip he took to Indonesia last fall for the wedding of a friend. No invite for you, he said. And there were more. Too many more.

Never. Ever. Again. I repeated silently to myself.

With unquestionable confidence I kept my perch on the piano bench, knowing *I* had done all *I* could do to save our relationship…and he had done nothing.

Synchronicities began occurring with such frequency that I was reminded of the line from Paulo Coehlo's "The Alchemist": "And when you want something, all the universe conspires in helping you achieve it."

For the last ten years or so, I'd considered myself a little more 'awake' to the signs and symbols—those messages that perpetually concoct ways to show us our life's path, our purpose. Pointing us in the direction of the best possible ride this lifetime has to offer. And sometimes the ticket to that ride is *more* than just a *little* uncomfortable to purchase.

It would be quite some time before I would learn of an acupuncture point called "Flagstones." The perfect portrayal of my synchronistic experiences that summer. Because with each step I took on my path towards my next beginning, I felt as if a flagstone was placed beneath my forward-stepping foot. The difficulty and discomfort came in un-weighting that foot, out of the known, swinging it forward and trusting in the presence of the next flagstone firmly fixed in the unknown.

After that May morning, the universe reignited its reveal. My lifelong goal to speak Italian by age 36, that deliciously melodious Italian, was closing in on its deadline. I was just shy of 35.

It was time.

The three months I continued to live in our house seeking a new direction weren't without moments of vacillation. At times they crept up ever so slowly, attempting to erode my resolve. At times they struck straight to the core of my being.

On one memorable morning I awoke paralyzed by the immensity of this decision and the words came to me, *may my courage be greater than my fear and may my trust be greater than my doubt.* Breathe. And repeat. And breathe.

Flagstones, I had to keep moving forward to find the next one.

The first one presented itself with exceptional clarity. I offered to make a delivery for my now ex-boyfriend to his new client, since I was headed that way. While on the road, my ex called me. "You're going to like this guy: he lived in Italy for seven years and just moved back to the States."

Italy?

Upon arriving at the quintessential New England country club with its Norman Rockwell-esque front porch dotted with welcoming rockers, I gazed across the beautifully manicured greens to the waterfowl-laden pond. Rising eagerness pushed me through the well-trodden threshold of the aged wooden door. Weaving my way along the thickly padded rugs that pointed like arrows down the hallways adorned with myriad paintings of the area's remarkable foliage, I peered into the gap between the windowed kitchen doors and my eyes caught sight of his crisp, white chef coat.

David had just returned from Venice, Italy. As we stood in that cool, brightly lit, stainless steel kitchen, I began to cautiously unleash the carefully curated questions I had created on the drive, hungry for information to pursue my dream to learn Italian. I left with his email address and enough information to fuel my fire.

After several emails, I convinced him I was serious and we met. He gave me two Venetian contacts: Gregorio and Alessandra. "Get in touch with them; they'll help you," he advised.

The span of time that followed possessed a significantly surreal quality. Although I felt fully present in my day-to-day life, I could sense a part of me beginning its move across the Atlantic. I was physically in Maine but energetically on my way to Italy.

I had made the decision to attend an Italian language school in Venice, *Istituto Venezia.* It sounded so sexy, just saying it evoked a presence deep within me. How this language seduced me. The simplest of words and expressions fell upon my ears with the same arousing effect of a soft, yet steady physical embrace made electric by the firm hand on the small of your back, silently suggesting the possibility of more as it draws you closer.

Having established an easy rapport with Betta, the school's secretary, I made arrangements to rent a room in the recently refurbished residence of a Venetian woman. Marina Fontana would be my new landlord. The promised photos never came. Instead, dreams did: so vivid and so real that I would awake confused as to where I was.

My plan, shared only with a few, was to stay. So, I began a little extra packing, just in case.

I made it to Boston's Logan Airport and discovered my flight to Venice had recently departed. Without me. Where was the next Flagstone?

My friend who lived in the city welcomed me up the creaky, curved wooden staircase of her classic Boston brownstone. We visited briefly as it was already quite late and both of us had big days ahead of us. Her, an interview for a new position. Me, well, just a new life.

As I loaded my luggage into the cab to Logan, the ache in my throat made swallowing difficult. Fear rose in my chest. Speech was nearly impossible. I so desperately wanted to reach out to my Dad. Don't do it, you'll crumble at the sound of his voice. I stared forward with teary eyes, struggling to take a deep breath in that dense, humid city air.

What am I doing?

August 31st, I awoke to the flight attendant's melodious morning greeting, "*Buon Giorno*". Relief, excitement and fear amicably co-existed within me as the tires touched the landing strip of Rome's Fiumicino airport. First stop: baggage claim. Within minutes, my enormous, Big Orange, stuffed-to-the-point-of-zippers-exploding suitcase with wheels and the tan canvas duffel resembling a human body bag slinked their way along the clicking carousel, followed closely by my over-sized money-maker, my sturdy, trusted massage table. Remember, the plan was to stay.

Back in Portland, my friend Paola had kindly coached me on how to say body parts in Italian. A seemingly odd start to a new language but perfectly appropriate for a massage therapist looking to start a business in *Italia*.

Customs, check.

Rental car, check.

Highway to Florence, check.

Five-hour car nap at the fanciest-roadside-snack-shack-rest-area, the Autogrill, check.

Disorienting arrival to Florence six hours past intended 1:00 p.m. ETA local time, check.

Local time. The time of one's locale. And what an endearing one Florence was. But the gnawing sense of urgency to get to my true destination, cloaked in the heaviness of jet lag, clouded my ability to take in the beauty of that lively city stacked with layers of history.

I steered the smallest car ever up the on-ramp of eastbound A5, my personal highway to heaven, with the Italian voices on the radio enthralling me the whole way. When the four-hour drive turned into seven and I still wasn't close to Venice, I wondered why I hadn't researched this leg of the trip more thoroughly.

After finally returning my rental car to the airport, my only option was a motor coach ride to Piazzale Roma, where this world meets the water-rimmed world of Venice. After I'd extracted my belongings from the belly of the bus with no assistance from the distant-gazed driver, I found myself in the middle of an empty cul-de-sac of asphalt, like the lone outfielder of a team that had gone home.

Just outside the closed ticket office, I located the schedule of the water bus lines, *i vaporetti*. My mind enlivened and the fatigue faded as I figured out which line to take and where to disembark. The silence surrounding me was broken only by the steady current of the water meeting the pilings. The air was thick and moist with a hint of salt. San Marcuola, the right boat had just pulled up. I leaned into the damp coolness of the railing. The gentle kiss of the canal on the vaporetto pacified me and withdrew from my being a deep sigh of relief.

I had arrived.

The boat and landing, *l'embarcadero*, squeaked in salutation. Now to connect with my new landlord. There, in the corner, a pay phone. Ring. Ring.

"*Si, pronto,*" she answered.

"Signora Fontana?" Although I couldn't comprehend everything she said to me, no dictionary was needed when she declared she was not Signora Fontana.

How could this be? Betta, the school secretary, emailed me weeks ago with my new landlord's phone number and address.

Breathing deeply to clear my muddled mind, my attention was captured by the lilting rolls of laughter weaving their way through sweet strings of this melodious language. Oh, the way it wove itself beyond my ears, playing me like Stevie Wonder played the ivories.

I followed the notes as if they were breadcrumbs on the stones. They drew me toward a hotel. The handsome, young man behind the elaborately carved wooden reception desk greeted me, "*Si, prego.*" I forced my tired American words, explained my situation to this kind-eyed man and inquired about a room. I was politely informed, in English, as the sounds of matrimonial merriment played in the background, that a wedding party had booked the entire hotel. He offered to look up my new landlord by her name; I eagerly agreed. It took a few calls to reach her mobile. His shoulders slumped. The recording stated she was either not available or her phone was turned off. This happens frequently in Venice due to the thick, stone walls, he said. On the last night of the International Film Festival finding a room would be challenging. He quickly called four hotels, nothing available. His last offering was a hotel on *Strada Nuova*, New Road, the main pedestrian walkway of this neighborhood and close to where we were. *Due passi*, he said, translating that to 'two steps', Venetians' unique way of measuring distance when on foot.

I had a feeling the next hotel wasn't exactly close. I yanked the extra large duffel up to rest on top of Big Orange and topped it off with the massage table; my computer nestled in my favorite messenger bag. Onward young woman, I heard in my head.

Ten minutes into my new journey to New Road, soft raindrops began to tap on the top of my head, and my forearm started to spasm. I couldn't loosen my grip on Big Orange's handle or the cobblestones would upset the delicate cairn of luggage I had created. Ugh, another spasm. How could I keep going? Nomads, think of nomads and their arduous treks, I thought. That idea worked for a bit. Think Gratitude, whispered a voice inside of me. I thanked God for keeping me safe thus far. I thanked the brilliant person who invented the wheel. This idea was mine after all. All mine.

What the hell was I thinking?

The faint, white letters on the shiny glass door told me I was at the right place, Hotel alle Guglie. The rain held a steady cadence but I didn't care. Exhausted, I left my belongings outside the door. With a quick glance at my disheveled pile of stuff, I started my ascent up white-carpeted stairs in that crisp alabaster hallway. They ended on a landing large enough for one. A voice came from behind the ornately wallpapered reception counter, "Si, prego." The words ignited a flicker of hope in my heart. I prayed for a better outcome this time. I asked if he had a room available. In his ultra-thick, R-rolling accent. "No, Signora. Sorry, no room."

Out came the tears. And they wouldn't stop. I could hear his voice through my sobs but they brought me no solace. His only offering was a chair in the lobby.

The visual of my luggage getting soaked in the rain snapped me back to the moment. Without saying another word, I ran down the steps and out the door. I opened my messenger bag, unzipped the inside pocket and there it was, the names David had given me. Up the steps I ran, skipping every other on my way, leaving soggy footprints on the pristine white carpet.

One of the names David had given me was Alessandra. And what a relief when she agreed to come get me.

My return trip to the meeting point was not without calamity, but when that Italian angel appeared in that empty cul-de-sac, I heard the heavens sing.

"Kimberly?" Alessandra asked with a subtle roll to the R.

I nodded my head, my eyes fixed on hers. How could I ever repay this woman? I could have been in danger, an exhausted, lone woman curled up on a pile of bags on the street at night.

Alessandra smiled and scratched her head, clearly perplexed by how I'd managed my pile of luggage thus far. The connection was instant.

She laid out the plan for the following day and said she would contact my new landlord for a time to meet.

When that time arrived, Marina was waiting at the gate. The clamorous cart made her chuckle. Each of us grabbed a bag as we ascended the three flights of steep, white marble steps.

Marina turned those solid-sounding tumblers with a weighted key large enough to not get lost in any sized bag. As that brilliantly painted crimson door opened, what appeared before me stole my breath. My new home was exactly as it had been in my dreams; from the white plastered cathedral ceiling to the exposed rough-hewn wooden beams, to the still life on the wall that drew my eye to the wispy sheers that played in the puffs of an afternoon breeze through the open terrace door. Yes, a terrazzo just big enough for me and my book.

How could this be? How could I have envisioned this without having received a single photo?

The room had an endless view of curved, terra cotta roof tiles of the city with the occasional bell tower standing tall with pride, ready to share its declaration of time. What am I doing? I thought as I lingered in that bed the following morning. Every cell in my body buzzed with an aliveness that prohibited any rest, let alone actual sleep. Thinking back, this arrival had been years in the making, fifteen in fact.

So in the faint light of the pre-dawn sky making its way through the white window sheers, I found a lightweight skirt and flowy tank for the slightly steamy early September morning. Sandals in hand so as not to wake the neighbors below, cautiously measuring each footfall on the smooth, speckled Venetian marble; my fingers found that key that opened that magnificent door. With excitement percolating, I swiftly made my way down those stairs, feeling the coolness of each step on the bottom of my toes. I quietly opened the gate that led to the alley that would take me There... wherever There was. Left? Right? Straight?

The pull was undeniable.

Left I went, all senses alit as I paused to slip on my sandals. As I passed each door and gate, my imagination conjured up visions of each interior. The mystery of each residence within those walls of stones hundreds of years old seemed to tap into the buzz that drove this early morning journey. Each stone on which I stepped brought with it thoughts of how many others had stepped upon it. And for how many years? I had never experienced morning dew on stones. It offered a sleekness, like a shine, that the stones wore quite well. As did the bridges.

The bridges. How many were there? Hundreds I had once read. Another wish to add to the list, discovering every bridge in this enchanting place. Up, over and down I never questioned which way to go. As I wound through the *stradas* and *calles*, the humidity hung gently in the air. Aromas of freshly baked pastries filled my senses as I peeked in each vacant pastry shop. Soon to be opened. but not just yet. Not a soul was seen as I continued on my way. Left? Right? Straight? Left again. And There it was.

Piazza San Marco declared the yellow-stenciled arrow on the cornerstone. St. Mark's Square opened to me in all its glory. In slow motion I glided beneath the arches. The promise of dawn peeked over the stately arcades of the buildings to the right and softly illuminated the office facades to the left. As the mere suggestion of sunrise began to touch the gold-gilded dome of the Basilica, the source of the pull stretched out before me. I felt myself move toward the center of the Square, not remembering a single step. A sense of calmness washed over me.

With an explorer's eye, I began an intentional slow circular journey taking in every marbled archway, every Byzantine window, every polished column. Off in the distance, in a narrow alley to the left of the Basilica were the silhouettes of two police officers, carabinieri, engaged in a heavily gestured discourse. The air hinted at a touch of salt rising from the lagoon. The soft kiss of humidity on my skin was welcoming and warm. The only sounds that found me were the gentle taps of the gondolas on the pilings.

Once I returned to where I began my circular exploration of *There*, which was now *Here*, the impulse struck. Without a second thought, I lay down on the stones beneath me and like a flash, as if I had just come to, *it* came to me. *It* came to every cell in my being.

I was Home.

———————✳———————

My Father, the Feminist

Judy Catterton

I never know what to say when people ask me: "why did you become a lawyer?" It's not because the answer is too long or too complicated. Nor is it because it's too private or too embarrassing. It's honestly because I don't know. Not don't remember. But truly don't know.

I do know exactly when and where the idea of going to law school first came up.

It was January 1970. It was three years after I graduated from the University of Maryland with a BA degree in English. It was also three years after I got married. It was six months after I left the General Services Administration where I had been a computer programmer. It was four months after my husband, Ken, and I, disenchanted with our lives and the war in Vietnam, left the United States and went to Europe.

Ken and I were camping in Europe in an old beat-up VW bus. I often refer to those days as our "hippy days." We had no itinerary, no particular destinations, and no date for return. We were living off our retirement money, both of us having worked for several years for the Federal Government where a certain amount of money was taken out of each paycheck whether you wanted it to be or not.

After arriving in Rome and locating a place to camp, we made our way to the Central Post Office. We had become accustomed to letting our parents know the next major city we expected to visit. They, in turn, sent mail with the direction: "General Delivery: Hold for pick up." After gathering our accumulated mail, we returned to our campsite. I remember to this day opening the letter from my father that contained his "proposal."

I knew before opening it that my father was distressed at our leaving. Vacationing in Europe was one thing. Travelling for your job was understandable. He, himself had sojourned in Europe for his work. But our trip was different. We had quit our jobs; given away our dog; stored our few possessions in my parents' basement; and said we didn't know when we would return. Worse yet, we said that we weren't sure we *would* return.

Sitting beside our VW bus on a hillside overlooking the beautiful city of ancient Rome, just as the sun was setting, I read my father's letter aloud. I really wish I had saved the letter since now I know it was the letter that changed my life. But here are the salient points: come home; Judy will go to law school; Ken will go to architecture school; and we will finish the basement of our house so you two can live there.

Here is what was wrong with this proposal: I had never expressed any interest in law school; Ken had never expressed any interest in architecture school; my parents' basement was far from "finished;" we had very little money and were in the process of spending what we had on our travels; my parents, though financially comfortable, were not by any measure well off.

The letter was so "my father." It was sincere, sweet, and logical. He tried to meet all our anticipated objections. My parents would respect our privacy. We would have our own entrance. Financial support would come from them as a kind of "pre-inheritance" inheritance, one that they would be around to enjoy.

I remember reading the letter aloud several times. We appreciated how desperate my parents were for us to return and how generous their offer was. But, we thought the idea was hilarious, completely out of the question.

And then, five months later, we did it. All of it.

When we returned home I applied to law school at the American University and Ken to the newly formed School of Architecture at the University of Maryland. Ken's father, a cabinet-maker by trade, was in charge of converting my parents' basement into a livable space, complete with a half bath and a small kitchen.

Actually, our kitchen consisted of a set of two burners, like a glorified hot plate, and a roaster oven, all sharing space with the family washer and dryer. My undergraduate grades were good enough for me to get a scholarship and Ken got a part-time job as a cost accountant at his old employer's firm.

I worried about how I would fare in law school. After all, it had been years since I had been a student. And then there was the added pressure of being one of only six women in a class of one hundred and thirty something. In those days we women felt as though we had to shoulder the burden of doing well both for our selves and our gender. After the first semester, my grades placed me first in my class; I was offered a Dean's Fellowship which involved a small stipend in exchange for assisting my Constitutional Law professor on a book he was writing; and I earned a full academic scholarship.

I had settled in.

Ken and I became kind of the "mom and dad" to a group of my younger fellow law students who were from out-of-town and lived in the dorms. I remember with nostalgia the evenings we took the door to my father's painting studio which was in our "apartment" off its hinges and propped it up with volumes from the 1956 Encyclopedia Britannica to create a table. I made potato salad while

Ken barbecued chicken on a grill my parents kept in their backyard. After dinner, we sat on the bright orange shag rug we had bought on sale at Sears to cover the tile floor in the living area of our basement apartment. One of my law school buddies played guitar while we sang folk songs by Cat Stevens and Jim Croce and something about a horse with no name riding through a desert.

There were times in law school when it wasn't so great being a woman. I remember the first year, in my criminal law class, the professor was going over the elements that comprised the crime of rape. He, no doubt intentionally, picked one of only three women in the class of fifty or so to interrogate. One of the elements of rape is "penetration" of the penis into the vagina. I remember him smirking as he asked a very attractive female classmate: "How much penetration, Ms. Cerna?" And when she didn't answer, he pronounced: "*Any* penetration, Ms. Cerna, *any* penetration at all!" These were the days when women thought we had to put up with that sort of offensive remark. We somehow were made to feel that we were lucky just to be there and complaining wasn't an option. After all, these were the days when it was lawful for universities to have quotas for the number of women to be admitted. These were the days when it was standard operating procedure for

newspapers to advertise separately: "help wanted men" and "help wanted women." So, Ms. Cerna shifted uncomfortably in her chair, forced a smile, and said nothing.

In the last of my three years in law school, I took a trial practice course. We were designated as Rule 18 students, a Maryland Rule of Court that permitted law students to try cases under the supervision of a licensed attorney. We spent one semester with a defense attorney and one with a prosecutor. After trying only a few cases, I was hooked. Terrified, but hooked: terrified at the awesome responsibility of representing either the State or a defendant in a criminal case; but hooked on the adrenaline rush of the drama of it all.

Though it's forty years ago and thousands of cases later, I can still remember the first time I spoke in a courtroom. It was a bond hearing in Upper Marlboro, the county seat for Prince George's County, which, though a suburb of Washington D.C., was at the time still quite rural. Driving to the courthouse, I passed acres of farmland where I could see tobacco hanging in barns to dry. Mere blocks from the courthouse were warehouses where every autumn auctioneers sold the dried leaves to cigarette manufacturers. In those days, several tobacco plants even grew in a cluster on the front lawn of the old courthouse, symbols of the County's lifeblood.

In the large courtroom where the bond hearings were held, the Chief Public Defender, remarkably for that time and place, a woman, stood next to me. She handed me one file from a stack of thirty or so and told me to argue for the defendant's release. I don't recall what I said or if I prevailed. What I do remember is that my knees knocked together; my throat went dry and seemed to close up.

After graduating from law school, it was time to search for a job. If you were a woman in the 1970's applying for a job and a man interviewed you, you were likely to get special questions, questions that only women were asked. I could almost tell when they were coming. The interviewer might pause, clear his throat, and shift his posture, as though even he was uncomfortable with what he felt obliged to ask. Here is a sample of actual questions that came from the "women only" interview drawer:

Interview with a County Judge for a law clerk's position: "Every year, I host a party for all my past and present law clerks. Sometimes, these parties can get a little raunchy. Would that bother you?"

Interview with a Maryland Appellate Judge: "Sometimes I work late in my office with my law clerk. Would your husband be bothered by that?"

Interview with a county State's Attorney for a job as a prosecutor: "Would you be comfortable trying a rape case?"

Here are my answers to these questions: "no," "no," and "yes." The "yes" wasn't entirely true, since I then had no idea what it would be like trying a rape case. If I were to answer now, I would say: "no one, man or woman, is ever comfortable trying a rape case."

When I was sworn in as an Assistant State's Attorney for Montgomery County Maryland, I was only the second woman prosecutor in the history of the County to hold that position. The first woman was a law school classmate of mine who preceded me into the Office by six months. We were a novelty at the bar. The reaction of the judges, the police, and the other lawyers ran the gamut. Some bent over backwards to try to let us know we were accepted. Some of the cops worried that we would not be tough enough. Some of the defense attorneys *hoped* we wouldn't be tough enough. Some of the judges didn't know what the hell to make of us. Some of the men in our world, and our world was mostly all male, thought we were there to flirt with. Others thought they had to be hyper-vigilant in what they could say around us.

Those of us "girls" who dared to play with the "boys" in their ballpark tried to fit in; not draw attention to ourselves; play ball as best we could. If cursing was needed, we cursed. If staying out late, drinking, was expected, we did. And yes, when men flirted we often flirted back.

In the beginning, trying not to draw attention to ourselves, we dressed in a way that approximated the way men dressed. We wore suits, with skirts that stopped at or below our knees; long sleeve blouses, silk, linen, or starched cotton, that buttoned up to our necks; and scarves we looped into bows at the collar to resemble men's ties. We went to court in panty hose and closed-toed shoes, wearing little make-up, and conservative hairstyles. Only after we were more sure of ourselves did we begin wearing more feminine attire.

I was a trial lawyer for over thirty years, nine years as a prosecutor and the rest in private practice. Mostly I tried criminal cases. But I also tried personal injury cases, medical malpractice cases, traffic cases, and civil rights cases. I represented doctors, lawyers, therapists, dentists, and nurses before disciplinary boards. I represented bail bondsmen, police officers, sheriffs, and even a few judges. And yes, I represented murderers, robbers, burglars, drunk drivers, shoplifters, and two men on death row. I represented the guilty and the not guilty. I tried cases before juries, judges, magistrates, and hearing officers. I tried cases in state courts and Federal Courts, trial courts and appellate courts.

People sometimes ask what it was like to be a trial lawyer. I'm not certain I can explain. It's like you see on TV and not at all like that. It's exciting, tedious, fun, challenging, taxing, and terrifying. Sometimes having the responsibility for someone's destiny is overwhelming. Once I represented a psychiatrist who would lose her house and all her savings if the verdict went against her in a malpractice case. Some of my clients faced losing custody or visitation with their children. And, of course, for many of my clients, their very freedom hung in the balance.

During the years I was a trial lawyer, I was married, had a child, a brother, four nieces, one nephew, two sisters-in-law, and one brother-in-law. For some of the time, I even had parents. I owned a house, went to dinner parties, saw movies and plays, took vacations, played golf and tennis, skied, swam, jogged, went to China, Israel, and Italy. And yet, my real life felt like it was in the courtroom. My clients' stories were *my* stories.

There were stories of men with guns who held up convenience stores. There were stories of young, angry boys who taunted the police and drove recklessly down residential streets. There were stories of drug addicts who valued their highs more than their freedom, more than their children's welfare, more than their very lives. There were stories of coaches who may have abused their students; of parents who hit their kids; of men and women who drank too much or fought too hard. There were stories of doctors who hurt their patients and of patients who lied about their doctors. There were stories of people who fought because they used to be in love and people who fought because they were enraged by the way some stranger was driving. There were neighbors who ruined property because a dog barked too loudly. There were people who tried to hire "hit men" to kill a spouse who had cheated on them. There were the stories of police officers who lied and police officers who died. They were the stories of life, their lives, but also my life.

Was I successful? How do I take the measure of that? Is it the amount of money earned? I definitely didn't make much money practicing law.

Does success lie in trying hard cases? If so, I tried my share of those. As a prosecutor, I was the Chief of a Major Offender Bureau, the unit that tried most of the serious criminal cases in the County. Does success lie in "putting the bad guys away" or getting the innocent ones off? If so, I guess I did my share of that as well.

If success rests in winning respect from peers, I venture to say, I did that too. I won awards; served on several Governor's Commissions; taught seminars; testified as an expert; was a consultant to the Office of the Public Defender; helped write two books; taught lawyers, judges, police, firemen, psychiatrists, paralegals, and toxicologists. I was honored to be the first woman president of the Maryland Criminal Defense Attorneys Association and the first woman Fellow from Maryland in the American College of Trial Lawyers, an association that is open only to the top four percent of trial lawyers in the country.

But some of the cases I remember now as successful are far more ordinary than the high profile cases, the "sexy" cases I often like to tell stories about. I remember a farmer I represented for some minor infraction who was the single parent of a severely disabled daughter. He paid me by showing up every Monday that summer with a paper bag filled with tomatoes, cucumbers, and green peppers. I represented a teenager in some juvenile matter I can't now remember. But I remember the beautiful white Afghan her mother knit for me when the case was over. I still have a cut glass bowl given me by an Iranian/American Army colonel I kept out of jail. Looking back on it now, I think there was great satisfaction in getting a troubled teenager to go to drug rehab or convincing someone with mental health issues to get into treatment.

In 1987, I visited for the last time a man I had represented who was under a sentence of death. Three days after my visit, he was executed. I was there to say good-bye to him. As a criminal defense attorney, there can be no greater failure than having a client executed. But at the end of our final conversation, he thanked me. I didn't understand. "We, your lawyers (there were several of us by then) failed you," I said. "I failed you." "No," he said, "you fought for me. You gave me back my dignity as a human being." Was that a success?

Should success be defined differently for me because I was a woman in a profession traditionally dominated by men? Do I deserve more credit than men of my generation because I had to balance being a mom and a wife with being a lawyer? I don't know. I do know that the balancing wasn't easy and I didn't always do it well.

As a woman practicing a profession in the last quarter of the 20th century, I learned to distinguish the difference between real prejudice and just male awkwardness; between flirting and lasciviousness; between references that meant, "you don't belong here," and those that simply meant "I don't know how to treat you." I learned that men were not the enemy. They too had been victimized by centuries of stereotyping. Men who were bullies were not necessary misogynists. They might just be bullies.

I never learned why my father thought I should be a lawyer. I never asked and he never said. I know this essay isn't supposed to be about my father. But in a way it really is. Feminism is not a subject that I recall being discussed in my home when I was growing up. But I think my father was an early feminist. I think he knew women didn't have only one of several traditional roles to play: wife, mother, secretary, teacher, nurse.

Maybe my father knew me better than I knew myself when I was twenty-one. He knew I loved words and logic; debate and argument. He knew I was interested in social justice and civil rights. He sensed that I liked figuring out what makes people tick. I think my father knew I was independent enough, strong enough, and yes, courageous enough to survive in a man's world. I think he knew, I would find a way, my own way, on my own terms, to be a successful trial lawyer. And, yes, I think he knew that I would love it.

————————✳————————

Each Leaf

letting go of its branch
takes a brave chance
that the air will cushion

its fall through autumn's
bronze light, sun still
in its veined heart.

It knows only
where it has been,
not leafspill, leafdrop,

not the milky sky at its back,
the world spun upside down,
and it must call forth

vast reservoirs of faith
to finally release
and trust

its solitary flight
and its far, uncertain landing.

Ellen Collins

A Damn Woman

Kathleen L. Martens

I'd never been called to the boss's office before. After a month on the job, the ride up the elevator in the new tinted-glass tower still gave me a thrill. Passing the color-coded floors that the architect had designed to parallel the shades of the earth, I rose from my mud-colored floor where I shared a four-person windowless office with three brilliant young men, each with some specialized PhD in engineering.

As I elevated from the bowels of the glass building, I thought of my challenging work—learning how to flowchart every step of my project; learning how to speak in acronyms; learning to fit into the sophisticated world of the renowned research organization in the booming mid-70's. I thought of discovering that a young guy with only two years of college was making thirteen thousand dollars more that I was, and the surprise at my immediate raise when I discussed it with the Senior Vice President.

In the times when corporate coffers were flush with profits, employees of Bell Labs flew first class on any business trip over 1,000 miles from our Headquarters in Piscataway, New Jersey; San Francisco had more than qualified. Memories of white linen table clothes, tiny little silver salt and pepper shakers and filet mignon served 30,000 feet up, still lingered. I felt beyond excited after my first business trip, my first class flight, the meetings with the executives, and teaching the administrative staff of Pacific Bell how to use their first big awkward desktop computer with the room full of massive humming and clicking equipment behind them.

While the men on my team taught the management and the senior executives; I taught the women in the office. While I ate sandwiches with the secretaries; my project teammates ate gourmet fare in the executive dining room. But the trip, and helping to make those women's jobs easier by the genius of their first computers was a thrill.

I wondered why I'd been called to the same Senior Vice President's office who had leveled the playing field and given me the raise. I thought maybe he was going to congratulate me on my recently completed assignment that my immediate boss had praised. It was a rare trip from the tan level floor to the sky box for a newbie like me; that much, I knew. And I'd heard that employees were often rewarded with AT&T stock when they did something noteworthy to move the organization even farther ahead into the cutting-edge future of technology.

The only woman with a mere Masters, the only non-PhD, I worked hard to cut it at AT&T's Bell Laboratories. I owed it to myself and to the friend of the family who did the hiring and had generously swept me away from the plum special education director's job I had found in the nearby county. Coming from a family of little means, I was lured by the salary, more than my father was earning, and far beyond a teacher's pay plan. I found myself in the Human Performance Technology Center; found myself in over my head. I found myself with a "future" as a business systems analyst. Whatever that was.

They had hired me to apply what I had learned in my graduate program in human learning to help develop training programs for the new Bell Telephone System to install the first computers systems across the country. It was a world of genius scientists and researchers, a world of unfamiliar rules and technical language, a world of men. I was unaware of the treachery of being a young woman in that man's world.

I elevated from the tan level, past shades of green, beyond the darker ocean tones to the senior executives' sky-blue suite with a beautiful bevy of butterflies in my stomach. The blades slid open to the all-glass suite with a panoramic view of New Jersey, and off in the distance the outline of the Manhattan skyline. Breath-taking; I was rising into heaven at twenty-two years old, in my man-mimicking skirted suit and not-so-sensible high heels, wearing my newly-trimmed long blond locks pulled back and twisted up primly. My investment in my new career. Could it get any more exciting; could my life get any better?

My boss's secretary offered me coffee, and I accepted. She hosted me into his office where he sat framed by a wall of glass with rolling green hills. The plummeting sun behind created a glaring glow around him. As a Catholic, I read it as a halo; and he had earned it.

Bill Scott was tall, and composed. He adjusted the family photo of his wife and children on his brown leather blotter with gold embossed swirls around its edge, and shifted in his chair. I began the think this was *not* an award ceremony.

"Kathleen, this is a delicate…well, I'm a pretty liberal guy, but…"

"Did I do…something wrong?"

His pause was painful and pregnant. He laced his fingers on his desk. My eye caught the twitch of his pinkie fingers. "Wrong, well…" The wheels of his high-backed, leather chair squeaked as he spun away from me, stared out the window, then turned back and took a breath. "Look, what you do is your own business, and I know you're, well, a healthy young woman but, Graeme told me that you slept with him on your business trip…and we just can't tolerate that. I'm sorry but I have to ground you from any future travel for the company."

My chair lifted off the ground as I rose. "What?"

"Graeme told me how you came to his hotel room in San Francisco and, well…you *lured him*, were his words."

I sat down, staring at my illuminated boss the sun now level with his head behind the massive window. I got it very quickly, my word against Graeme's, a brilliant essential man on the team, me one of only three women in the entire building who was not a secretary. I searched my mind for what to say. I thought of Graeme, all 5'4" of him. He was a nerd before the word became sexy. He stood nose to nose with me, his extreme under-bite, his bulbous body, poor personal habits, taped-up broken glasses. Well, honestly, it was hard enough being beside him on the plane.

I felt the moisture erupt on my forehead. I leaned forward to appeal to my boss, and fought back tears. *No tears in the workplace*, I told myself. Then, I stopped and pictured Graeme in my mind, and literally shuddered at the thought. The idea came to me. It wasn't what I would normally say or do but I was up against the wall, desperate, and unfairly accused. I don't remember clearly thinking it through; the words just came. "Close your eyes, Bill. Trust me," I said.

He shrugged, cooperated, and nodded.

"Now picture, Graeme. Got it?"

He nodded, seeming to get impatient.

"Now picture *me*." I took a deep breath. "Please forgive me for saying this, but if I had the choice of the hundreds of men in this building…I really feel terrible saying this…but do you really think of all the good-looking, attractive men…including you? Bob Waring? Chuck Marley?" I named some attractive candidates. "Would I really choose Graeme to have sex with?" I was uncomfortable even saying the word "sex" sitting in front of my boss. But this was my future, my integrity on the line.

He opened his eyes and I could see my simple logic light up his face with relief. He picked up the phone and Graeme arrived shortly to sit beside me. Under interrogation, he confessed to Bill it was all a rumor he had spread to brag around the water cooler.

Graeme was grounded, taken off the project, and I was promoted in his place. Liberty and justice for all in the 1970's.

Well, not quite.

Weeks later, just before installing a new nationwide program, all three male project team leaders left for new jobs. I was twenty-two, the grunt, and the only one who knew the details. Bill moved me up to the top floor, yes, an office on the sky-blue floor across from the boss who had saved my career. With no other good choice, Bill sent me to present the new program to a sea of silver-haired executives in Dallas, Texas. I was so nervous. He advised me to imagine everyone in their underwear, and start with a joke.

My secretary used only my initials in all correspondence to arrange the trip. She said she didn't want them to know I was a woman so they couldn't stop me from coming. I was learning.

During the entire flight I tried to think of the joke; I couldn't get my head around the underwear advice. At the airport a man in a suit was holding a cardboard sign that said, "Mr. K. Kempshall." They clearly did not expect a woman, especially not a *young* woman, the age of most of their daughters.

"I'm K. Kempshall."

"Did he bring his *secretary*? We weren't told."

"What are we going to do with *her*?" one of my greeters said to the other. "Where is he, the men's room?"

I informed him that I was the person they had come to retrieve. They mumbled to an assistant, and their look of panic made me smile.

I was brought into the exclusive good-old-boys' men's-only club for my speech hunched over with a sport coat over my head through the kitchen door. Mortifying. As a liberal New Englander, I was not prepared for the cultural difference in the country called, Texas.

"What's that damn woman doing here? No secretaries allowed," was my greeting as I entered the room.

Pressure built behind my eyes. I quickly imagined the group of well-suited men in underwear, not a pretty sight, stepped to the mic, and told the joke. "You may have noticed I'm young..." I heard a chuckling in the crowd, but I knew they were snickering at me, not at the opening to my joke. "Bet you're wondering why headquarters sent a young woman for this critical project."

They laughed, commiserated. Nudged elbows into each other's ribs.

"Well, I was the only one they thought could handle you." I paused, took a huge risk, "I have a Master's Degree in Special Ed."

A second of painful silence. Then, uproarious laughter. Buh-dum-bum. I had their attention. Luckily, I knew my stuff. They peppered me with questions, but the presentation went well.

Later, relaxing by the hotel swimming pool, the men teased. "Bet you ten bucks you won't jump off that three meter diving board."

I looked up. "Are you kidding, no way."

They egged me on, reached for their wallets and upped the ante, tossing the money mockingly on the table under the striped umbrella. 100 dollars, a fortune back then. After taking their increasing goading, something began to build inside me. Like the entire female gender's pride was at stake.

I climbed the ladder shaking, looked down, wrapped my arms around myself. The warm Texas sunset illuminated my performance against a raspberry and orange western sky, and the hot metal steps encouraged me to move back gingerly. I retreated. "I can't," I whined.

They taunted, hooted and hollered.

I shook my head, no.

They punched each other, laughing. "Come on, girl!"

They wanted to see me make a fool of myself. That hurt the woman in me, the child in me. My Dad had always told me I could do anything. I climbed the ladder determinedly, stood straight-armed Olympic-style on the diving board, and paused for their taunting. Peering over, I saw their jeering faces, took three strides, lifted one knee, sprung from the board, did a perfect one-and-a-half in pike position, no splash, just like I had done in the county diving championship.

The last thing I heard as I entered the cool water was a deep Texas twang, "What the *hell*?"

Emerging up the steps, I flipped my long "dumb-blonde" hair, swept the hundred dollars off the table like a croupier in Vegas, and strutted away leaving a dozen eyes bulging, mouths hanging, and me grinning.

"Little lady...you...hustled us!" the ring leader complained.

Yes, gentlemen, you've been *had* by a *damn* woman.

———————✳———————

Undressed

Christy Walker Briedis

Michael carefully packed the floral-patterned suitcase for her, the one with wheels so she wouldn't have to struggle over curbs. It had a long extension handle which was just right for a woman as tall as she. He could envision her parking their Buick La Crosse at the beach front hotel, close enough to the ocean to smell the freedom of salt air, opening the door and stepping into the sunlight to stretch and smooth her skirts, pull her fitted jacket to her waist, and adjust her Coach handbag over her elbow. He would remind her to leave the heavier luggage for a porter.

He tried to choose her favorite clothes for this anticipated annual trip to Rehoboth. He gently folded them, appreciating the soft fragrance in the lacy lingerie she kept tucked into her drawer with the sachet that permeated her delicates. He packed newly purchased packages of nylon stockings, a few scarves and a shawl, in case it became chilly, and skirts that would sway when she walked the streets, brushing against her long legs with a satisfying whisper. There was a second bag for her shoes, oh, she loved having the choice of sandals or heels. Which one would feel right at the moment, which color, which style, a peep toe or a strappy bronze affair to show off her latest pedicure? Her style wasn't racy, it was classy, "bandbox" his mother would have said, and always feminine. He alone had seen all the lacy bras and pastel panties with bows or small gems, tastefully hidden from the public. Like a thin sugar coating on candy, they were the last layer over her inside secrets. He recalled the first time as a child he had fingered these sensuous fabrics, restricted to women. His mother kept her long gowns in his childhood closet, where he liked to hide, his face buried in the cool silky folds of fabric where her perfume lingered. Yes, he remembered that.

He opened the quilted leather jewelry box and selected her favorites to store in the cloth oriental cinch bag she preferred for travel, with little compartments to separate earrings and chains, the center cavity for her gold bangle bracelets. He slid her many rings on a long slender tube, secured by a small brass snap so they would stay organized once the pouch was cinched by its satin cords. In Rehoboth she would surely leave this satin pouch in the hotel safe, it represented a large investment from their earnings, although money was not a concern. Keeping her in style, adorning her and indulging her whims, this thrilled him in a way he tried to keep to himself. She was going on this trip without him, of course, this packing ritual was his way of giving her his blessing. As Michael made his final offering, he unzipped the side compartment of her handbag, slipped in his driver's license, some cash and from a locked desk drawer the secret credit card he had acquired for Melissa.

Finally, smiling to himself in anticipation of the long awaited weekend, he added her printed invitation to the Second Annual Cross-Dressers Convention, and firmly closed the door to the empty apartment.

Leaving the rural roads of Pennsylvania, the Buick merged into highway traffic much in the same way she merged into the larger world outside the confines of her hometown. She traveled to Delaware via New Jersey where she was not likely to be recognized. Her favorite hair salon kept her appointment time with generous leeway in case she was delayed by traffic. Melissa always left one or two of her wigs there, the stylists would always create the newest and most flattering hairstyles for her. Usually this required a phone call to them the week before so she could she could discuss her travel plans, so her hair matched her intentions; it could be a trip to NYC for Broadway shows, or to the photographer for her planned session in a wedding dress, and now, a casual weekend at the shore. She could be assured that they would generously give her use of their large lady's room to change since her traveling clothes, a tweed sports coat and freshly creased chinos, were not in sync with her new hairstyle.

It was remarkable what was available in the ladies' room of a quality salon, perfumed pump hand soap and assorted lotions, hair spray, cotton balls and sometimes make-up samples. Melissa never used these, she preferred the services at Saks Fifth Avenue. The Estee Lauder counter was already scheduled for her make-up consultation. It amazed her how many different products a woman needs to maintain her flawless complexion. Subtle cheekbone enhancement and the eyes were practically an hour by themselves. She always made the clinician's efforts worthwhile, purchasing some new cosmetic promise every time, not to mention the latest in lipstick shades, Caramel Latte, Parisian Promise, and her favorite Mango Mystery.

She knew, a real woman is never without lipstick. She had recently read that when Jennifer Aniston is too rushed for make-up she will just put on one of her large pairs of sunglasses and her signature lipstick color. Well, yes, if you looked like Jennifer Aniston you could do that, but it was an important beauty tip from a Hollywood star.

After her hair appointment and her make-over, Melissa strolled into a crowded nail salon in the New Jersey mall. They loved to do her nails because she required those expensive nail extensions and she loved the time and effort these Vietnamese ladies took with her. Melissa was never impatient; after all, this was the event. The workers chatted endlessly with each other in meaningless sing-song that she was able to ignore so to better watch the other women getting their manicures and pedicures. Some chatted away on cell phones while their feet were pampered, some gingerly turned pages of Cosmo as their nails dried. She watched with her measured eye—exactly how they turned magazine pages, crossed their legs, touched their hair, kept their sweaters over their shoulders or lifted coffee to their lips. Ahh, the nuance of feminine behavior. There were always tips to learn in these places where women congregated, where their most natural actions flowed, where they interacted with each other unrestricted by the presence of men. She hoped this would reveal the essence of the feminine mystique; hand motions, head tilts, adjustments to hair and clothing. If she could capture these details of feminine behavior, possibly, she could move among them and be accepted. She knew this was a challenge due to her height and strong masculine features, some of her cross-dressing friends actually passed, but they tended to be smaller and fine featured.

Melissa came into my boutique on a sunny, cool Friday afternoon in October. She was with a small group of others from the convention, similarly made-up and over-dressed for our casual beach town. A charming, outgoing retired couple from Iowa had driven their camper this far for the cross-dressing convention, held annually at an ocean-side hotel up the street. They happily gave me their calling card, "The Flaming Farmers", and laughed explaining they always wore the same thing, purchasing two identical blouses, one in his size one in hers.

My store was located on a secondary street well-known for alternative behavior, so it was not so surprising to see cross-dressers, but to see them shopping in my store was new. Melissa and her friends were carefully touching and commenting about merchandise in a way that invited the saleswoman in me to approach them in the gender they presented. We spoke about colors for the season, they lamented 7th Avenue's preference for pants over skirts, they considered the complications of jumpsuits and see-through blouses. We discussed tank tops as undergarments, Spanx for body contouring, and costume vs real jewelry.

As the others drifted out the door Melissa lingered. She softened her undisguisable deep voice, and asked for some personal shopping assistance. For privacy, or was it a desire for discretion on my part, we made an appointment for the next morning an hour before our normal opening time.

At six foot-two without her preferred 1 ½ inch heels, I guessed her to be a trim size 14-16 and preselected items I thought would fit.

She arrived at nine, smiling with a sweet acknowledgement of her special treatment. After wandering through the store she took her additional selections and meticulously drew the curtain to the dressing room. She used a net make-up shield to cover her head, so none of her heavy make-up got on the clothes, and she took care to be tucked in, buttoned up and presentable each time she stepped out to our large public mirror waiting for my approval.

Over the five or six years she made her annual trip to our town, I came to know Melissa's style and favorite colors just like any of my other customers. I tried to be honest about how her choices fit or flattered her, how they enhanced or hindered the image she wanted to achieve. As she became more comfortable in the intimate space of my small women's store she allowed herself to mingle with other shoppers and remain in the store during the normal opening hours, offering comments to other customers.

As her comfort level rose, mine fell. What would be the reaction of my clients, their husbands, my employees? Would they leave, make comments, or worse, be unkind?

I tried to present myself as the open, accepting, worldly woman I thought I was with few hang ups about personal lifestyle choices, but I feared my efforts were as transparent as Melissa's attempts to pass as a woman. I struggled with my discomfort. Beyond some street exposure—same sex couples holding hands, kissing on benches, unusual clothing or barely any at all, I knew little about this world. Intellectual acceptance did not always translate to my gut.

When I got to know Melissa, I recognized the loneliness, guessed the shame and secrecy of her obsession, came to appreciate the power of this desire that put her job as an engineer, her personal relationships, and her safety in jeopardy. Working on this street for so many years it was impossible for me to ignore the drive-by comments, or the drunks who threw beer bottles from their trucks, or the late night assaults on men whose appearance challenged the norm. The frequency of these incidents on our street were greatly reduced, but that didn't end the threat.

On one of her visits, she called and asked me to join her for dinner, leaving the time and location to me. I considered the choice carefully. I made reservations for an early seating at a chic restaurant near her convention hotel, hoping she wouldn't be hassled or shamed when she used the lady's room, or reapplied her lipstick. I hoped from previous exposure, the staff wouldn't stare when a six foot-four inch heavily made-up man dressed as a woman with big hair and a soft swaying walk ordered a Manhattan and drank with a poised pinkie finger.

We were seated by the hostess in the center of the restaurant at a small table. The lighting was subtle, the flowers and cleverly folded cloth napkins set an elegant tone. As we waited for our cocktails she removed a small enameled metal disc with a hook from her bag which she placed on the table.

"See how you can hang your handbag from this hook?" she chattered in her deep voice. She delighted in showing me how to hang a purse as the counterbalanced weight held it off the offending floor. We laughed at the tricks she had learned from her recent observations, and she offered to buy one for me.

I had come to truly care about Melissa and privately worried that she was lonely. She never spoke about a romance, and always traveled alone. Imagining what would make her happy, I asked, "do you have someone special at home?" Before allowing her to answer, I suggested, with naive ignorance, that she might find the right *man* someday. Melissa straightened in her seat, her large, beautifully manicured and jeweled hands gripping the edge of the white tablecloth, looked at me in astonishment and said, "I'm not gay."

My suggestion had clearly put her on the defensive and I could only meekly reply, "Oh, I didn't know." Clearly I didn't understand at all.

She told me with regret about the woman Michael had been engaged to, the love of his life. This woman had accepted his feminine side, his pleasure in cross-dressing, and they got engaged. Until, her adult son found out and swore never to speak to his mother again if she married Michael. The wedding was off, the relationship ended.

Melissa's shock at my ignorance was the catalyst for some research, soul searching and much stretching of my rigid assumptions. I was surprised when I read several online sources suggesting that cross-dressing is not an uncommon practice by heterosexual men. I couldn't find an explanation, or even a commonly agreed upon word to describe this, were they cross-dressers or transvestites? It confused me. Did they want an intimate relationship with women or men? How does it start? Why does cross-dressing compel them when the dangers, physical or emotional, in a traditional society could so injure them? I had so many questions there were no answers for. The one that haunted me the most was, why was I so uncomfortable?

Years passed. I didn't see Melissa as often; the cross-dressing convention had discontinued. At the store I received occasional phone calls and Christmas cards from her, and when she visited again we had dinner. I was prepared this time to ask some intimate questions about the why and how of it. I was ready to be honest about my own questions. She trusted me, now I have to ask her to trust my intention to understand her choices. As we ate together, Melissa told me she had always admired women, their grace, their strength, their style, their options for self-expression through make up, hair styles, endless clothing options. In her view, these were ways to present one's creative self, the softer self to the external world. Her secret had caused her much shame so that twice in her life, in an effort to be rid of the compulsion, she had thrown away all of her tools of transformation, various wigs, make-up, endless shoes and clothes, only to begin again. Yes, she struggled with acceptance in love, and secrecy at work, but now in her 60's she tells me she accepts that part of herself.

Shortly after our last meeting, Michael retired from his career and I retired from mine. A final letter arrived from Melissa's post office box. She told me something wonderful had happened to her, and she was moving away, closing her secret mailbox and would, sadly, never be returning to our town. She was so excited and happy for this new life she was pursuing and wanted to tell me how my acceptance had been such a joy in her life. And that was all she said.

As the days dwindled toward my store's final closing, I packed up what remained of the inventory. I wandered over the bare wooden floors of the nearly vacant rooms now littered with empty boxes for final packing. I remembered the many deliveries by our cheerful UPS driver, the daily excitement of opening each new collection, the satisfaction of arranging appealing displays, fully accessorized outfits with scarves or jewelry, shoes placed on acrylic risers on the floor below, and the final pleasure of sending off each piece in yellow wrapping tissue sealed by a gold logo sticker and packed into the store's signature red bag.

My final few boxes sat on the empty floors with packing tape nearby, ready to be filled for donation on our last day. I removed odd size dresses from wooden hangers, wondering why the perfect someone didn't buy them before we closed. I folded them into the box. I sorted T-shirts in last season's colors, automatically turning the sleeves to the middle and folding each in half before adding it to the box. I packed jeans and jumpsuits, maxi dresses and beach hats, costume jewelry too fancy for the beach, and bangle bracelets too small for women's wrists. These lone items were all that remained of the options I had offered to transform the thousands of customers who had walked into my boutique.

From my desk I gathered the papers I wanted to keep, treasuring the letters from customers over the years. Letters that told me stories of the dress they'd worn to a bar where they met their future husband, or the wardrobe that took them stylishly around the world, the woman who finally found something to fit that had made her feel beautiful. And I found Melissa's letter, reminding me of the universal desire of my customers, no matter shape, age or size to stand in front of the mirror and experience that magical transformation. To embrace a new vision of themselves, just as Melissa had.

Seeing her letter, I remembered I couldn't even write to her, since she left no forwarding address. I couldn't even tell her what she had done for my life. How she had opened my mind or was it my heart?

It was a quiet, rainy day in the fall when I closed my store for the final time. I saw the wilting, long stem peach roses with the farewell and thank-you sign on a small table in the window. I saw the curtain-less dressing rooms, bare racks, floors and walls, bare for the first time in over three decades.

I placed the letters in my tote bag and adjusted its weight over my elbow, pressed the small brass button on the handle of my umbrella and pushed it open, selecting keys from the interior zip compartment. Before I closed the door to my empty store, I glanced back one last time. I saw my reflection in the only remaining fixture, the large wall mirror, where for years, customers had stood transformed by their time spent in the dressing room. And I pictured Melissa among them. As I stood looking back at the mirror, I knew I also had been transformed by my years standing behind them.

———————✳———————

The Garden Goddess

Aphrodite stands proud among the maiden hair ferns. Her clay neck is scarred and her arm wears a canvas sling. The man and woman of the house had found her in the morning lying in the rose bushes next to the gate. They patched her broken arm with mortar and cemented her back onto her pedestal. She heard the pity in their voices as they blamed the storm that had downed branches and toppled trees on the boulevard. They wouldn't think to ask a goddess where she'd been. And they wouldn't have believed her if she'd told them how she'd scaled the fence and sashayed down to Eighth street for a change of scenery last night. She was bored with the doves and sparrows and rhododendrons that had no personalities. At the first disco she'd let down her toga, danced nude on the tables, laughed as the men clapped and called her *ecstasy* and asked to take her home. But, like Cinderella she had to leave before dawn and get back to her garden. She had to be on the pedestal and have the urn in her hand before the woman came out for the morning paper. In her rush, she'd tripped over that damn dress, hit the pavement, and broken her arm. No, the wind or the thunder hadn't crushed her bones—but she didn't regret the wine, the music, the men, the sip of life—and who was she to spoil their myth?

Sherri Wright

Dreamer in the Nursing Home

At night she dreams
in her railed bed in the corner room,
and sometimes she trembles,
and sometimes she sighs,
but always in the gray dawn
remembrance of those dreams dissolves,
ephemeral as wisps of fog.

Yet, one night, restless, watching
the moon pasted on the cold sky,
she sees it wink at her,
and she heeds its invitation,
slips out to the parking lot,
trading flannel and chenille
for silk and patent leather.
The crooning trumpet of Guy Lombardo
guides her feet over gleaming parquet,
and artificial stars circle around her head,
a diadem of champagne bubbles.
A hand at her back warms her,
and not once does she slip or falter
or lose the beat, and her lips curve
into a smile as she sings show tunes
she thought she had forgotten.

In the morning,
when sun stripes the blanket over her legs,
the metal sides of her bed are locked and firm,
her cane across the room leans by the dresser,
and she wakes exhausted.
Her feet ache, her voice is hoarse
from laughing,
and she cannot explain
those pale pink rose petals
curled in her hand,
that twist of ribbon
behind her right ear.

Ellen Collins

———————✳︎———————

afternoon

shafts of sun
frame the site

old women sit
in dappled light

soft voices murmur
of times now past
where life's illusions
were unmasked

simple needy
lonely hard

all dust and heat
the sound of birds

jahill

Sex on the Sand

On the shallow slope of sixty, this slide
into old age, I wonder, in an idle way,
as we stroll along the water's edge,
what it would be like if we mustered up the grit
to have sex here on the sand, yes, sex
on the sand, before it's too late,

before we shrink, become another old pair,
two gray silhouettes curved over silver walkers
as we make careful passage down railed hallways
for the four o'clock serving where table talk starts,
stalls, then settles on portion sizes, ailing joints,
who will succumb to the cherry cheesecake?

Will we rue the day we turned down the chance to play
Burt and Deborah, find our own secret eternity
on the sands of the state park, where the waves pummel
the shoreline, where we would have unzipped, stripped,
sprawled on some illicit dune, flushed and breathless,
ignoring the sand needling our sweaty skin.

Well. This is how I imagine it. In truth,
sex on the sand is just a reckless notion, like sex
on the kitchen table, or sky-bound in the jet's lavatory,
or pinned to the walls of a high-rise elevator,
a titillating story to relish, shock old friends.

Now, on the shallow slope of sixty, our limbs
no longer stretch and straddle at will, prefer to lie
on a sleep-numbered mattress with clean cotton sheets.
For now, for us, the ceiling fan dispatches
a gentle breeze, the noise machine from Walmart
whooshes ocean sounds, and the two of us sink,
as always, into a familiar pattern of flesh upon flesh,
a cushion for all that comes next.

Irene Fick

This poem was first published in *Gargoyle* in January 2016. It has also been accepted for an upcoming anthology: "Unmasked: Women Write About Sex and Intimacy After Fifty," scheduled for publication this Spring by Weeping Willow Books.

※

Asunder

Divorce is a moan in the night
and when that moan swells
to the wail of a stale country song,
divorce is that song played over
and over as you cruise in a borrowed
old Buick down a single
lane road, and divorce is that road
that dead-ends into a splintered
split-rail fence, and that fence flanks
a small patch of land left untended,
and when that land swallows
itself into a sinkhole, divorce pushes
you down until there's nowhere
to go, and when there's nowhere
to go, you collapse at the bottom,
and when you collapse at the bottom,
you shatter into pieces, then you clutch
those pieces to heave and claw
back up, spitting dirt all the way,
and when you do that, you find
that asylum of sunlight, that funnel
of air, and that's when you begin
to breathe.

Irene Fick

This poem was first published in 2015 in *Adanna Literary Journal* and won first place (single poem) in the 2016 Delaware Press Association contest, and second place from the *National Federation of Press Women*, also in 2016.

〜〜〜〜〜✳〜〜〜〜〜

Slow Dancing with Strangers

Sarah Barnett

We've gossiped and exchanged Christmas gifts over soup and salad at Panera. Next stop: Famous Footwear. My friend Polly rummages through her large leather handbag in search of lipstick. "You never know," she says, as she repaints her lips in bright pink, "Mr. Right may be in there."

In the shoe store? Do we never stop hoping for romance?

We try on several pairs of shoes and boots, but no Mr. Right appears to admire my new red suede pumps. That doesn't stop me from believing that *someone* is around the next corner, and it's only a matter of time before we bump into each other.

In the movies they call it "meeting cute," as when Hugh Grant accidentally spills orange juice on Julia Roberts in *Notting Hill*. The reality—awkward blind dates, wondering will he call or won't he, responding with just the right blend of smart and sexy to a match.com ad—is messy, difficult, undignified.

Secretly I believe that it is all still possible—the glance across the room; instant attraction; falling into something bigger than yourself. After more than 20 years of single life, I still find myself looking. I'll recognize him when I see him. Over there, no wedding ring, drinking espresso, reading The New Yorker; he's about my age; he could be the one.

He could also be a serial killer.

When I was first divorced, I was pretty sure I'd meet someone, and one thing would lead to another. Maybe we'd dislike each other at first á la *Pride and Prejudice*, but we'd come together with the help of some really clever banter.

Some people make it look easy. My friend Sandi found herself divorced and raising three children under the age of seven. "I can't go anywhere. I'll never meet anyone," she wailed. "Who would ask me out?"

Guess what? The UPS man asked her out.

These things do not happen to me.

Here is what does happen: A sunny June day in the *Home Depot* parking lot. I'm wrestling two large patio chairs into the trunk of my Toyota Corolla. No matter how I arrange them, some arm or leg hangs out, preventing the lid from closing. Behind me someone says, "Need help?" Wearing jeans and jogging shoes (and no wedding ring), he carries his own purchase in a bag that might hold a couple of bolts or paint swatches. He attempts all the configurations I've already tried.

"That won't work," I say, as trunk lid crunches chair leg. He tries again, and again, while I fidget. "It's okay," I tell him. "I'll drive home with the trunk open. Thanks for trying."

"Yeah, well…" He makes a vague gesture at chairs and trunk, picks up his purchase and heads to his car.

Once more I tackle the mass of arms and legs. I lift everything up, give it a good shake, and magically, the chairs settle themselves in place as if they were waiting for Mr. Not-Quite-What-I-Had-In-Mind to leave them alone.

How did I completely miss the "meet cute" potential here? I hear my mother's voice as it occasionally pops into my head: *A nice looking man offers to help you, and you make fun of him? What's wrong with you?*

She's right. Why didn't I think to ask him if he'd like to take a coffee break? My friend opened the door to the UPS man with a smile, but my first instinct was to slam down the trunk lid and turn away with a scowl. What was that about?

As a married woman, I couldn't help envying the independence single women took for granted. I admired the smart, spirited women in novels, who tossed out husbands as casually as they'd throw away milk that's reached its expiration date. Kinsey Millhone, Sue Grafton's private detective, for example. You won't find her at a New Beginnings workshop trading bad date stories with other hopefuls. She's busy hunting down deadbeats, not obsessing about finding another mate.

Living alone after 30 years of marriage, I walk the fine line between loneliness and solitude. I want a body in my bed, a greeting when I come home from work, someone who'll hand me a cup of coffee in the morning, someone to hand a cup of coffee to. Yet, the quiet of the empty house soothes me. No hidden resentments lurk in corners. No crumbs on the kitchen table, no half-filled coffee mug in the sink. Does the absence of these things spell freedom? Freedom, which I now see offers both benefits and limitations—fewer responsibilities but little that anchors me to the real world.

I told myself I wasn't ready. It was never the right time—too busy, too fat, having a bad hair day. I wanted it to be easy—to exchange a look, feel a spark, he'd feel it too. We'd circle each other, chat a while, then one of us would move off, always returning to the same spot where we'd continue talking as if no break had occurred. We'd go somewhere for coffee. The next day he'd call for a date.

I want to be home in front of the TV, watching *When Harry Met Sally.* Instead, at 10 o'clock on a Friday night, I'm at a singles dance in a suburban

American Legion Hall. I've prepared carefully—four shades of eye shadow, two coats of lash-lengthening mascara, sleek black pants, turquoise silk shirt, sparkling earrings. I stand near the wall, waiting for a total stranger to ask me to dance.

I say yes to Steve, who moves us in ever diminishing circles, so that pretty soon we're practically standing still. While Percy Sledge sings *When a Man Loves a Women*, couples conduct the *whatdoyoudo? wheredoyoulive?* exchange, the dialogue resembling a job interview or the series of questions and answers in my high school Spanish book (*Como está usted? Bien, gracias...*).

Get busy, I told myself. Take a trip; plow through the books piled by your bed; organize your photos; take up bonsai; learn to knit, needlepoint, embroider (too little- old-lady-ish?), bake bread; take tennis lessons. There was plenty to do. But it was filler, what people did to pass time until, when you weren't looking, when you had given up, you went to your Italian class and there he was.

I dance with strangers and they remain strangers. Enough, I tell myself, staying away from singles activities for weeks, then months. Ten years pass. I'm in my early 60's when I attend my last singles event with my friend, May—a kayak trip on the Chesapeake Bay. We are the oldest women there.

Prince Charming is not coming. He sent his regrets. A blizzard, a plane unable to land in fog, a sick relative, a pile of proclamations to sign. Or, he simply did not exist. I consider some of the men I met in this 20-year Odyssey: Dave, who dressed in a cow costume (black and white with udders dangling from his belly) at his summer party; Hank, who phoned to say I'd missed out on the dozen roses he would have sent after the big date I'd refused. John, who used up all the air in my living room, who inquired about the cost of every item in my home. And don't forget Harry Homeowner, who couldn't make the chairs fit. My mother would say I'd been entirely too picky. I can hear her now, "You're no bargain, you know."

Guilty.

It's temporary, I told myself. Single life would be a partly enjoyable, interim phase, which, when the novelty wore off, would be replaced by a loving relationship with a suitable male.

Should I have looked harder? Was I just plain scared? It's no accident that we call it "falling in love" and don't we know how dangerous falls of any kind are to people of a certain age?

What now? Give up? Forget about it? That might work. I'm getting good at forgetting things.

How easily temporary became practically permanent.

For all my cynicism, I still believe that love is possible—that feeling of plunging into the unknown, the imagined conversations, the real sharing of intimacies. I have no trouble imagining that someone is waiting for me. A sweet guy in jeans and a sweatshirt might help me pick out a garbage disposal at Lowes. Or he could be trying on jogging shoes in Famous Footwear.

———❋———

Private Dancer

I want a black leather mini skirt
like the one Tina Turner wore
when she sang Private Dancer in 1979.
I want that pelt to fit like the
rind of an orange over the curve of my hips,
I want it to twist and talk
with every move. I want to yank
that skirt over a little tank top
fringed in sequins and beads that shiver
and shimmer with every exhale. I want to
dance long bronze legs into my
daughter's classroom, rock past the hippie teacher
and roll right up to her smarty friend who lives
in the big house on the lake—that girl
who walked into my bathroom,
helped herself to my lipstick and polish
and was amazed that my daughter and I
cooked dinner, set a table, and sat down to eat.
With my little mini, I will shimmy,
into the office of the counselor who wrote
"broken home" into my 3rd grader's
permanent file.   I will close the door
swivel my hips onto his desk, look him
in the eye, I will teach him what a "divorcee" looks like,
any music will do.

Sherri Wright

———————✳———————

No Magic Words

Nancy Powichroski Sherman

My mother stands ankle-deep in the white foam of the ocean with her arms purposeless at her sides. I contemplate whether I should put down the article I've been trying to read and join her, but I can't bear her usual silence. I'd rather sit here in my beach chair and remember conversations that Mom and I had in better days, or compose new ones where I, like a solo chess player, create both sides of the dialogue.

Her sagging back peeps past the deep purple of the skirted swimsuit. She would never have chosen such a suit for herself, but now she lets me buy her clothing and dress her, a grown-up doll that has replaced my mother. The irony is that as a child I never enjoyed playing with dolls. From the time I could sit up on my own, I paged through color illustrations in the Golden Books that Mom placed in my hands. When I was old enough to follow storylines, I listened as she read classics to me: *Heidi, Anne of Green Gables, Little Women.* She taught me my love for words. Not just for the power of their meanings, but for their sound and how they feel when spoken. Perhaps that's why my favorite curse word got its place for the way its ending "k" smacks the top of the mouth when said. I used to keep a journal of words on pages titled *Pretty, Exotic, Smart*—titles that might have fit who I wanted to be. Now, I have a short list that contains only two words, yet they crowd my mind. The category is *Contemptible*, and I have scrawled into it *dementia* and *Alzheimer's.*

Mom waves at the seagulls gathered on the wet sand, and they scatter into the air like her memories of my brother and me. She calls Chris "that nice young man." I don't know what she calls me.

My brother is late for his shift on the beach. How long can it take for a simple grocery run to Lingo's for enough food to finish what's left of a two-week beach rental? Vacation is such a misnomer; it can't be a vacation when neither of us is truly free of our burden. "Burden," I say aloud to feel it in my mouth. A two-syllable word, each part beginning with a plosive sound, smacks against the air. Being a caregiver sometimes feels this way to me. I wonder how long Chris and I can handle the month-to-month trading game we play as we shuttle Mom, her meds, and her suitcase across Philadelphia from one life to another, like divorced parents sharing a child.

Mom turns and looks in my direction. Her eyes speak only clouded messages that I cannot decipher. Still, I dutifully put down my magazine and go to her. "Mom? Do you want something?"

She looks past me at the cottage as though I'm invisible, and perhaps I am, then she turns again toward the ocean. Like Odysseus' men responding to the Sirens, she moves to voices that only she hears. To get her attention, I pick up a purplish seashell from the soft mud and show it to her. "Do you remember how many of these we used to collect each summer? And how we let them dry on the windowsill of the cottage, yet they still made the car smell of seaweed on the way home?" She accepts the shell and closes both hands around it.

The sun loves my mother's hair. It sends sparkles of light across the silvery threads that have thinned in the past few months. Her crowning glory, no longer thick and auburn, offers little cover for the now-locked vault of her mind. Sometimes, I still believe that I can find the key that will unlock that vault, but my own mind is tired. I yearn to return to the beach chair and the comfort of reading. "Where is Chris? Why is he taking so long?"

"Chris," my mother repeats, and though I feel sibling jealousy that she says his name and not mine, her speaking encourages me to move forward, an Ali Baba in search of the magic word to unleash her memory.

"Mom, do you remember coming here each summer and how we read on the front porch of the cottage on rainy days and told each other about our books?" With no acknowledgement that I spoke, she bends over and pushes her clasped hands through the tiny wave endings, never letting go of her captive seashell. "Mom, do you know that you gave me my love of books?" I feel my chest tighten. "And my need to see the ocean every summer? Do you know that you gave me that?" I don't know whether the moisture gathering on my face is the ocean air or my own emotions. "Do you know that I love you?"

"When can I go home?" she asks, and, though disappointed that she didn't say, *I love you, too,* I am grateful for a whole sentence.

"When Chris gets back from the grocery store, we'll go inside the cottage and have lunch."

"My mother and father will worry about me," she says.

My heart does Morse code inside my chest. A conversation. I'm having a conversation with my mother. I remember what I read in the articles that poured from my printer when I googled Alzheimer's after Mom was diagnosed, and I tell her, "Your mother and father know that you're here. You'll be with them soon." When I was ten and my father passed away suddenly, my mother told Chris and me a story about golden gates on top of a puffy luminous cloud where smiling faces of angels wait to greet us when we die. Back then, it helped. Now, I wonder if there is such a place.

Mom's face is a mix of child-like eyes in a wrinkled face, a crazy cut-and-paste portrait against the blue wall of sky. "I want to go home," she says.

I exhale, "Me, too." Not to my condo in the city, but to that cottage of past summers, the one with the window seat that held a view of Silver Lake, the one where we were all young, healthy, and happy, and Mom was a brilliant linguistics professor at Villanova raising her children on her own, a widow too soon. Chris and I were disappointed to find that the old cottage had been bulldozed. We had no choice but to accept this newer beachfront house with all its modern amenities. But it doesn't have our memories absorbed into its wallpaper.

Again, Mom bends over to slide her hands through the water. A wave splashes at her calves, and she giggles a little girl sound.

I never wanted a child. I could never have handled raising one. I have no list of words entitled *Motherhood*. What I say and do come from suggestions in articles I've read, not from any maternal instinct supposed to be part of my DNA.

I hear a car and look toward the cottage, hoping to see my brother carrying bags of food up the stairs. When I turn back again, my mother is knee deep in the water, several feet from me and just beyond my touch.

"Mom! Don't go out any farther."

She doesn't stop her slow wade to deeper water.

"Damn," I say, as I toss off the cropped jeans that cover my swimsuit. "Mom, wait!" I call to her. She is now waist-high in the water. "Mom, where are you going?" I call as I push through the chill of the waves that climb from my calves to my thighs. I grab her arm. "Mom, come back in."

She's pulling from me and saying something, but her mumbled words disappear into the sounds of the waves. Her strength belies her age, and I don't know if I'll be able to get her back to the shoreline. This private section of beach is coveted by most visitors, but at this moment, I wish we had stayed in one of the boardwalk hotels where I could get help from the lifeguards assigned to the public beach.

"Mom," I plead and once again search for the *Open Sesame* that will get her attention. I try, "We need to look for Chris."

She's pulling harder, and I begin to think that she'll drown and I won't be able to save her. Our tug-of-war is taut and exhausting beyond my tapped energy. Fear radiates up my arms and down deeply into my gut, and the torture of anxiety becomes worse than the idea of death.

I let go.

She stumbles, but she doesn't fall. She walks a few more steps, while I stand motionless, a silent observer. I watch as the taller waves split around her, spreading their fingers through her glistening hair. She is beautiful, like Venus on the cover of a Roman mythology book she used to read to us.

I don't move. I separate from the scene before me. This is a movie, a Fellini film, full of poetry. It's not real.

The shout of "Mom!" breaks the air, but it's not my voice tossing her the life preserver; it's my brother's voice. I hear the splashing and watch him skip-run in a diagonal toward our mother. When he reaches her, he takes her clasped hands into his own and, stepping backward like a strange sort of folk dance, he leads her to the hard wet mud of the shoreline.

I remain in the path of the waves, letting them toss spray against my back and watch my brother wrap a towel around our mother. "She might have drowned," he shouts. He helps Mom into her chair and sits on the sand at her side, a kind of *Madonna and Child on the Beach*.

My adrenaline drops, releasing my knees and making the walk to the chairs as awkward as my search for what to say to my brother when he asks, *why didn't you stop her?* I could tell him that I tried. I could tell him that she was stronger than I. I could tell him that I no longer know what to do or when. That I can't do this anymore. That we need to consider nursing care for her.

Mom opens her hands, and Chris accepts the seashell she gives him. "Very pretty, Mom."

"Very. Pretty. Mom," she repeats, and nods, and smiles.

It is the smile that I remember from behind the opened books of my childhood. If a heart can break, her smile is cleaving mine. I can't put her into a nursing home. I can't put her away like an aged book too fragile to be held. Not with that smile. I know that I'll never find the magic words to bring her back to us. I know that I'll mess up again, that I'll let go of her hand. But that smile. I could never let go of that smile.

———————✳———————

Six Days in June

Rosa M. Fernández

June 20, 2016

This morning I was putting on my rings and noticed my hands. They are starting to reflect my age. Soft veins gently pop out of the tops. I like them. They remind me of yours.

Four nights ago I lay in bed with you watching the Yankees play the Twins. The game had been delayed due to rain and you'd been impatient for it to start. We had only ever watched a game together when it was the Yanks and the Os. We'd smack talk about our teams being the best and yell at the TV as if the players and umps could hear us.

Friday night was different. You didn't understand what was happening in the game and I had to explain to you who was at bat, and the score (for the sixth time), and that it was the bottom of the 8th (two strikes, one ball). You, a man who often bragged you started playing baseball in Cuba with your nine older brothers before you could even walk. You, a man who talked about Joe DiMaggio as if he himself taught you how to hit a grand slam.

I was next to you trying to keep you calm and dispel your hallucinations of a shadowy hand reaching through the window stealing things from the dresser, and the people in the mirrors walking beside you. I tapped all over the mirrors and looked behind them and searched the windows. I told you I didn't see anything, but maybe we should check in the morning when there was more light. It seemed to calm you a bit.

I sat on the bed with you. I had to touch you, Papi. I held your hand and caressed its beauty. Dark and spotted. Large veins looking as if they were about to burst.

Hands that had delivered hundreds of babies and comforted countless mothers whose babies died. Hands that cured our wounds with merthiolate and band aids. Hands that picked peaches and pears and apples from the trees you had planted and cared for as if they were children. Hands that had built two beautiful gazebos where the family socialized in the summer and napped on the large hammock that swayed because you had attached a rope to the wall so we could pull it and rock it ourselves. Hands that hold your granddaughter's faces as you tell them how beautiful and smart they are (when you remember who they are). Hands that will forever be lovingly imprinted in my memories.

Is it true we are "blessed" to have had you for so many years?
Is it true it will make your passing less painful?
Is it true you will be forgotten in a couple of generations?

June 21, 2016
I drove down Rt. 1 South this evening enjoying the warm breeze caressing my body through the open windows. I inhaled the smell of steak coming from a dozen different restaurants that pepper the sides of the slow moving traffic filled highway. It made me think of all the family cookouts we'd had throughout so many years.

Where we grew up, you built, with your own hands, the outdoor grill from white bricks (to match the house) and red tile inside (to match the roof). It was indeed a work of art.

The three grates sat waiting for the steak, chicken and pork that would soon pour their smoky perfume into the yard where we kids played baseball or soaked each other with the hose; our appetites whetted by the smell of your grill. You were always in charge of the outdoor cooking, even the corn boiling in a gigantic aluminum pot sitting on the gas stove you placed next to your barbeque grill.

Now we are in Annapolis and those years of youth are as unreachable as one of your softball-size peaches at the very top of the tallest tree. You are still the master of the grill. The family gathers in the hot summer sun seeking shelter under the deck where you have placed numerous chairs (are there ever enough?) I am happy to sit at the long picnic table you built, feeling the sun massage my muscles and roast my skin like a lizard baking on a rock.

Was it only three years ago that you burned the meat for the first time? Was it only three years ago that Pete had to start helping you with the grilling because you would forget to turn the meat? Was it only two summers ago that you cooked out for the last time?

I can still see you in your faded green polo shirt and jeans, wearing the New York Yankees apron I'd given you for Father's Day (even though I hate the Yankees.) You are holding the spatula up as if in salute and smiling proudly, your black-silver hair reflecting the sun's brilliance.

I wish I had known it was the last time.

I would have eaten more slowly, savoring the love in every morsel, every bite. I would have done more than thanked you for the wonderful meal and kissed your cheek. I would have given you an enormous hug and told you that you were and would always be the King of the Barbeque.

And now you can barely remember you have to go to the table to eat the dinner Mami has cooked for you.

I wish I had paid more attention.

June 23, 2016

I sit in Grotto's with my friend, Lin, waiting for the torrential rain and bombastic thunder to blow out to sea. The ubiquitous TVs are tuned to numerous sports channels. Do they ever turn those TVs off? Can anyone have a conversation with that incessant noise? Will the electricity please go off so I can hear the rain? I try to not pay attention because none of them are showing an Os game anyway.

I move beside Lin so I can see the downpour through the large window whose view is distorted by the waterfall of rain. I realize I have become a woman of extremes. If it is going to rain, then let it be a deluge. If it is going to snow, then let it be a blizzard. If it is hot and cloudless, then let the sun permeate my skin.

It wasn't like that when I was a child, the youngest of five. We had escaped Cuba and were living in Mexico. My siblings had been sent to America to a foster home until there was enough money for us to join them. I was too young to go along. I was frightened by the storms that hit during the rainy season we spent there. I could see the lightning on the wall through the slats of the blinds and the bare mattresses on the floor that had once nestled my sisters and brother. The thunderous blasts made me cover my ears and cry. Mami would come get me and lay me on the bed between the two of you. I would curl in safety as you laid on your side and covered my ears with your soft hands.

When I went home for Father's Day last week, it rained so hard it sounded like the tat-tat-tat-tat-tat of a machine gun on the skylight. The electricity went out and I rushed my way towards you in the dark, feeling the walls beside me. You were already in bed and as I entered your room, the generator kicked in and the lights came back on. I could see the panic in your eyes.

"Are you okay, Papi?"

"¿Que Paso?" you asked.

"Didn't you hear the thunder?"

"No, I didn't hear anything, but I saw the helicopter lights. They are spying on me again."

I knew it was useless to try to convince you it was just lightning. I asked if you wanted me to stay with you for a while and you said "si." I curled up beside you on your bed. I would have put my hands over your ears, but you couldn't hear the thunder anyway.

June 24, 2016

I am the first car stuck waiting for the train to cross the main street in Georgetown, Delaware. It is a slow, long train, but I don't mind. I turn off the ballgame on the radio so I can hear the train and hang my arm out the window to feel the sun's heat. I have always been fascinated by trains and thrilled by their sounds. They transport me back in time.

Once a year in the 1970s (was it really that long ago?), we'd take a long awaited two-week summer vacation in Miami to visit family and swim in water so clear you could see fish gliding around your feet. We often took the Auto-train. I believe my love affair with trains began during that time when we would sit in the glass observation car and watch the world rush by, and slumber to the train's gentle rocking and repetitive sound as it skated on iron tracks.

I believe you had a love affair with trains too. Years ago you bought a large, expensive train set that smoked and had a loud toot which sounded when a red button was pushed. You said you bought it for the granddaughters, but I knew you really bought it for yourself. The girls lost interest in it very quickly anyway.

But you and I? We could play with it for hours; changing the direction of the trains by a mere push of the controls we held in our hands. We watched them enter and exit tunnels and go up and down mountain paths. We could make them go slow or fast and make plumes of smoke come out of their smokestacks by adding extra oil to them.

A few years ago, you lost interest in your splendid creation and underneath the table; stored Christmas decorations began to encroach the space. You sold the train for pennies on the dollar.

Do you still remember the times we spent playing with them?

Do you still miss them?

Do you even remember what a train is?

June 26, 2016

Today I am finally unpacking from my visit home for Father's Day (a task I have been avoiding.) It is hot as hell up here. The windows are closed because of the threat of rain, and the fans only circulate hot air.

Why are you starting to give away your possessions, Papi? And why, despite my protestations, do you want me to go through your extensive DVD collection and take whichever ones I want? I take a few to placate you. As I unpack, I see the Ken Burns documentary on the history of baseball I gave you a few years ago. It is still in its plastic wrapper. I take a sip of water because suddenly it feels as if I can't swallow. ¡Ay Papi, como te extaño! I miss you.

June 27, 2016

I pass my little wooden kitchen table on which I have placed family pictures and never use as a kitchen table. I glance at them and see the black and white photo of your latex gloved hands holding a shiny baby still covered in his mother's blood. It represents not only your life's work, but life itself. Many years ago you were the only OBGYN in our small county on the eastern shore of Maryland. You delivered most of the children during that era. I still have people ask me if I am your daughter and when I say yes, they often say you delivered them or their children or grandchildren. I always feel so proud to be your child.

You used to remember that photo well and said you told the mother this boy was going to be the next Joe DiMaggio. You probably said it to all mother's who'd given birth to sons, but you never told us that. Each of my siblings has a copy of the photo as do you in your home office.

Do you remember that recently I went in there to make sure you were drinking the water your doctor said you must drink throughout the day to stay hydrated? I handed you the picture and asked if you remembered it.

"It's somebody holding a baby. Why is it so bloody?" you asked.

"Papi, those are your hands. You delivered that little boy."

You put your glasses on and look at the picture more closely, scrunching up your nose. "Is that one of the girls?"

"No, you have granddaughters. This is a boy."

"Oh, I don't remember that boy."

Why can you not remember that strikingly beautiful picture of the beginning of an existence?

Why can you not remember the countless lives you helped bring into this world?

"It's okay. Maybe he is now the best Yankee since Joe DiMaggio."

"Who is Joe DiMaggio?" you ask.

"Never mind, Papi. Just some guy who used to play ball."

———————*———————

Gaining Wisdom

Marion Winslow

My childhood as a chicken farmer:
I started early. My Grandma owned a small chicken farm about a mile from my house. Every morning, rain or shine, Mom straightened the house, dressed me, and we went "back home"—as she called it.

When I began school, nothing changed, except that I had to walk to Grandma's house after classes ended. I loved it, especially in the spring when Grandpa received his order of baby chicks. 150 soft and alive little balls of yellow down, all chirping at once. That was the best time of year!

However, they grew up into chickens. At first they were fun to hold (Grand-pop did not appreciate my help). Then, too soon, they were big and allowed to roam outside in the yard. I thought it was great fun to chase them around... until Grandma caught me. Evidently my childish antics were not helpful to egg production—often the eggs had blood in them (my fault?). The chasing stopped.

As I got older (and more sophisticated) I became bored with chicken-play. The chickens, of course, were delighted I was gone.

My next big experience was "candling" the eggs, by putting them in a round hole with a light under them to find the eggs with blood spots in them. Those eggs were kept for the family. I didn't appreciate that and it took years for me to get used to eating eggs containing blood spots.

I was in 2nd grade when it finally dawned on me that Grandpa actually 'killed' the chickens and sold them to people for dinner. I found out by accident. Usually the job was done early in the morning, when I wasn't at my grand-parents' farm. However, one night Mom and Dad had to go out, so I was taken to Grandma and Grandpa's house to stay overnight. I woke up to a lot of clucking and screeching and "hammering" (actually it was Grandpa chopping off heads in the chicken yard). Being young and naive I thought we were being invaded by robbers stealing the chickens and killing them! My mind was soon changed as I looked more carefully out the upstairs window and saw dozens of headless chickens hanging on the clothesline outside. I immediately climbed back into bed and wouldn't get up. This traumatic event faded slowly from my mind and I finally understood the meaning of "roast chicken".

I used to help Grandma prepare the eggs and chickens for delivery on Saturday morning. And then go with her to deliver them. It took quite a while to get used to *Grandma* driving. Women just didn't drive cars in 1938!

My Grandparents influenced my childhood to a very great extent. My Mother was always there, but she knew who was "Boss"—my Grandma!

Lifestyle Changes:

The most important time of my life—when it was completely changed and led me to the path that I have continued to follow since—occurred when I was 17 and a student in the nursing school at Hackensack Hospital in Hackensack, New Jersey.

I had just finished my first year of training and had been "capped" in the school program for Nurses; I was ranked in the top 4% of the class.

My "best" friend was Ginny Nelson, a classmate of mine. We were preparing to be room-mates as we moved into the second stage of training. I was *so happy*!

One afternoon, shortly before we were to register for classes, I was told by a nasty girl (who knew how much her words would sting) that, instead of me, Ginny had selected 'Pat' to be her room-mate and had already moved in with her that day.

Let me remind you, I was 17 and very shy. My reaction? Well, at that age the experience devastated me! I was devoted to Ginny. How could she to this?

So, in desperation, I walked away from nursing school that day and was too proud—and embarrassed—to ever return.

I returned to a career in modeling for a while, and later got a job as an analytical technician at Uniroyal (fortunately I had enough science to do the job). As always, life holds many surprises, this is where I met Don. The rest is history—63 years of marriage and three children, a B.A. in elementary Ed.—and a truly wonderful life.

My First Christmas:

It was the first Christmas Eve of our marriage. The whole Winslow family was there for the traditional Christmas Eve dinner at his Mother's house. She and I had always gotten along but there never was any real "closeness". We were both "polite".

After dinner Don gave out gifts. Everyone "oohed" and "aahed" as each was opened.

He saved mine till last. "Mom" and I sat together, and both of us expected that I would get something very special. My new husband handed me a beautifully wrapped gift box tied with satin ribbon. I could not wait to open it.

After everyone guessed what it was (Jewelry was the best guess) it was time to find out. He had wrapped it *very well* and it took time to unwrap it.

Finally there it was—in all its glory—an electric frying pan!

There was total, stunned, silence. I looked at Mom—she grinned, I smiled back, and then we both began to laugh. I threw myself into her arms and we were both helpless with laughter. We were close now, and understood each other a lot better.

I have to thank Don for it all. Poor Don—after 63 years, I still don't think he gets it.

Making time for Cancer:
Being diagnosed with breast cancer, (one-year *after* my husband had been told he had prostate cancer), then falling down and breaking my leg the following week, was somewhat of a catastrophe. Here I was, all booked for breast cancer surgery, with a broken leg!

It was a stressful time to tell the truth. I had the leg operated on at AGH and then went to Health South for rehab. All Cancer surgeries were pushed back until I recovered from fractured-leg surgery. By the way, it was our 52st Wedding Anniversary!

Poor Don—Poor Don—he really had lots to handle, plus he was still dealing with his own Cancer issues. It certainly was a lot for us to manage, as well as an exciting time to get through, to say the least, but, we did it together!

Growth:
In my life I have gone through a complete change of attitude. When I was young (and even as I got older) "hugging" was "just not done". I always felt (and was told by my Mother) that hugging was just too personal. People did not appreciate that much closeness. And I believed that for many years.

My 180 degree turnaround started when I was diagnosed with Cancer. Going to Cancer support meetings opened my eyes. People actually *liked* to be hugged, and to my surprise, so did I. After the initial feeling of strangeness I felt warm and loved (or at least liked) by the people around me—an entirely new sensation for me.

Now I enjoy the closeness I once pushed away—the warmth of someone's arms enfolding me lets me know I am accepted as a friend.

My thoughts on the Central Park Jogger:

Before we moved to Ocean Pines twenty years ago we lived in Connecticut. While there I became very active in the Gaylord Hospital Auxiliary. It is a well-known nonprofit rehabilitation hospital, founded in 1902 as a treatment center for tuberculosis. Eugene O'Neill was its most renowned guest. In the 1950's Gaylord turned to other forms of rehabilitation......pulmonary disorders, strokes, spinal cord injuries and brain tumors. The 500 acre campus is set in the hills of Wallingford, Connecticut, flanked by a golf course and woodlands. In 1989 it became the home of the "Central Park Jogger".

This was the first time since I had been volunteering that we had this much excitement and publicity about a patient. She was a young woman from New York who had been savagely attacked, allegedly by a group of 14 to 16 year old boys, in Central Park. The cruelty of the attack was horrendous. She was found naked, except for her bra, which was pushed above her breasts. Her running shirt had been used to gag her and force her into a praying position. She had been raped and sodomized. When found, she was bleeding from five deep cuts across her forehead and scalp—people who lose this much blood generally die. Her skull was fractured and her dislodged eye had to be put back in place.

Permanent damage seemed inevitable. The attack hit the headlines, and for weeks this was the biggest source of news. The extreme swelling of her brain from blows to her head made brain damage almost inevitable.

Her arrival at Gaylord was quite an event. We were all told, "Treat her like any other patient, but, do *not* make any mistakes, and do *not* let any of the press into the building!"

Thanks to a wonderful staff her recovery was like a miracle. I only saw her from a distance, but the fact that she is now leading a normal life is due to the care she received in Gaylord.

The Bathroom:

One thing mattered more than anything at this time—the *bathroom*!

We found that water had seeped into the flooring and it had to be replaced. But that's not all—We took out the Jacuzzi and replaced it with a 6 ft. by 4 ft. shower with 5 water sprays in the one end. Also, we had heating elements put under the tiled floor.

Wow! Sounds wonderful doesn't it? And it will be in two to three weeks. But right now we have to use the upstairs tub and shower and the downstairs powder room for makeup, shaving and whatever—you know what I mean. I have trouble climbing the stairs because of my back, and going up and down is not easy. I considered giving up showers, but I decided, if I did, I would not be very popular with people, including my husband.

So, I will have to "bite the bullet" and just walk up and down at least once a day. You cannot believe how anxious I was to get back to normal again, after I fell down those damned stairs. Oh, did I forget to tell you about that?

It's Hummertime:
April is an exciting month for those bird lovers in Maryland who wait impatiently for the return of the Hummingbirds. Don and I start washing, filling and placing our feeders out around April 20th. We usually see the first hummer very soon after that.

My cat Shana thinks it's an exciting time too. She knows something is coming to the bright red feeders hanging just out of her reach on the porch Windows. As the hummers slowly begin to arrive she watches with great interest and a quivering of her tail as they perch. They seem to know she's in the house and harmless, and she has learned from trial and error not to jump up at a closed window.

As the season progresses we have seen what we call "hummer courtship". There are a lot of erratic flight patterns as the males try to impress the females with their abilities. Then things settle down until the babies arrive. The males guard each feeder and chase all others away. It can get pretty exciting. They fly so fast they sometimes miscalculate their objective. One hummer, heading for the feeder missed it and ended up with his beak caught in the screen on the porch! Fortunately Don was there to rescue him. He flew away crookedly but seemed to be all right. (At least we didn't find a dead hummer in the yard afterward)

I truly look forward to their annual arrival. I'm now counting the days though, and by the latter part of the month our fun will be put on-hold, in anticipation, for the next 'hummertime' season.

Guilt:

Guilt is a five letter word that has a very important meaning. Everyone experiences guilt of some sort. Perhaps you forget to do something that you were supposed to do, you are late for a meeting, (or worse, you forgot about it!), you unintentionally hurt a loved one, you know about these 'guilt provoking' situations….

That is normal guilt, and is something everyone deals with, at different times in life, everyone faces some type of guilt—self-imposed, or guilt someone tries to thrust on you. But there is another type of guilt. It is a feeling you have about something or someone that you cannot control. It eats at you night and day, and you become obsessive about constantly turning it over in your mind. The worst kind of guilt is about something that happened years ago, and you have no chance of correcting the situation or changing the outcome.

The problem is—from my 85-year-old vantage point—learning to accept the guilty feeling, realizing you cannot change whatever originally caused the struck-on guilt, and then moving on with the rest of your life. Otherwise it is always there, a constant haunting thought of, "How could I have said that?, or, Why did/didn't *I do* that?, or, Why couldn't I have done something?"

Most people eventually learn how to deal with these feelings, but not everyone. Those who cannot, spend their lives saying, "Why did I do (or not do) something when I was able to?

Nothing good comes from this, but, here's the trick: acknowledge the 'stuck' place you're in and move on with your life.

Lots of luck with *that* idea, it's not a simple feat! However, if you take the time to *see* what occurred, and try to *understand* what happened, and acknowledge your part (intentional or not) of the awkwardness, and then—this one's not so easy either—accept the fact that life goes on, regardless of what you did, or, didn't do, in other words, how you handled it, I've found that a sense of peaceful forgiveness will always plant its seed.

~~~~~~~~✳~~~~~~~~

Stand Up, Speak Out, Fight Back: Using Your Divine Femininity!

Ruth M. Alcorn

Most of us have heard of the 1911 NYC fire known as the Triangle Shirtwaist Tragedy, in which 146 women and girls died because there was no way out for them—the doors on the upper floors were locked and there were no fire escapes—the trapped workers were burned alive!

Headlines screamed the news of the inferno that had swept through the upper floors of the factory and Americans were horrified by reports of the tragedy. Ironically, many of the workers had participated, the year before the fire, in an unsuccessful strike over the same unsafe conditions in NYC factories.

The Women's Trade Union League, with the support of sympathetic wealthy society women, Anne Morgan (sister of millionaire banker J.P. Morgan) and Alva Belmont (activist and socialite), to name just two, had, because of the dreadful safety issues, used their influence to publicize a strike in 1910. The work stoppage gained improved conditions in some, but not all, factories, and helped some, but not all, factory workers. The owners refused to acknowledge unions, yet met enough demands to stop the strike, which ended in February 1910. The deadly fire broke out near closing time on March 25, the following year.

Mary Jones, a union organizer who gained prominence during the Haymarket Riot of 1886, had become known as "the most dangerous woman in America"—a phrase coined during her 1902 trial for ignoring an injunction banning meetings by striking miners. Reese Blizzard, a West Virginia district attorney, is remembered for the distinct compliment he paid Mary Jones (although *he* didn't consider it a compliment at the time!). Later she was denounced on the floor of the U.S. Senate as the "grandmother of all agitators." Mary wasn't on hand to help with the 1910 strike in New York, but she has gone down in history as one of our most effective union organizers—this little lady made quite a difference!

Charismatic Mary Harris was an American school teacher, a dressmaker, wife and mother. She is, however, better remembered for her efforts to improve the lives of factory and mine workers and their families. At the age of sixty, she effectively assumed the role of 'Mother Jones' as she cared for women, children and 'her boys' in factories and mines throughout the U.S.

Born August 1, 1837, in County Cork, Ireland, Mary emigrated with her family to Canada when she was fourteen years old. She later moved to the United States where she became a teacher. Always on the go, Mary moved to Chicago and then to Memphis, where she married George E. Jones, a member and organizer of the National Union of Iron Moulders. She opened a dress shop in Memphis just as the Civil War began.

Mary lost her husband and their four young children during the 1867 yellow-fever epidemic in Memphis. After that tragedy, she returned to Chicago to open another dress shop. That establishment was destroyed in the Chicago fire of 1871.

Mary Harris Jones, barely five-feet tall and weighing less than one hundred pounds, devoted the remainder of her long life to improving the lives of factory and mine workers. This unlikely leader, from 1897 on, was known as "*Mother Jones.*" She fearlessly grew into her role as a prominent labor and community organizer who co-founded the Industrial Workers of the World (IWW).

Mother Jones was considered "*the most dangerous woman in America*" because of her success in organizing mine workers and their families against the mine owners. In 1903, upset by the lax enforcement of child labor laws in Pennsylvania mines and silk mills, she organized a Children's March from Philadelphia to the New York home of President Theodore Roosevelt. Permission to see President Roosevelt was *denied*.

Mary believed that 'no strike has ever been won that didn't have the support of women.' She would tell the men to stay home with their children as she created an army of miners' wives wielding mops, brooms, and washtubs, and marched them to the entrance of mine after mine. The women knocked down the guards, scared the mine mules, chased strike-breakers, and caused pandemonium. Her organized strikes were successful!

Want an example of Mary's grit? Here's a copy of a letter this feisty woman wrote to Colorado Governor, James H. Peabody, on March 26, 1904:

Mr. Governor, you notified your dogs of war to put me out of the state. They complied with your instructions. I hold in my hand a letter that was handed to me by one of them, which says "under no circumstances return to this state."

I wish to notify you, governor, that you don't own the state.... I am right here in the capitol, after being out nine or ten hours, four or five blocks from your office. I want to ask you, governor, what the hell are you going to do about it?

Mother Jones

"PRAY for the DEAD, and FIGHT LIKE HELL for the LIVING" became the battle cry of Mother Jones—those words are still invoked by union supporters to this day!

The magazine Mother Jones, (MOJO), established in 1970, is named after Mary Harris Jones. Each issue focuses on themes that were important to Jones: corporate and political corruption, social justice issues, unfair wages, etc.

Note: The first newspaper reference to her as '*Mother Jones*' was in 1897.

Did you know?

The word '*feminist*' first appeared in print in 1885, describing a woman who "has in her the capacity of fighting her way back to independence."

———————✳———————

Dream New Dreams

Carole Schauer

Much is said and written about "grief"—a response most often caused by a loss. No one escapes it because everybody will lose something, whether it be the death of a loved one, loss of a job or a home, or living with an injury or illness. Perhaps for some, most difficult of all, coping with a broken relationship.

But there is a special kind of loss that doesn't get much attention—that of the death of dreams. Losing the possibility of what might have been becomes the cruelest loss of all because it takes away hope.

We have images in our mind of what the future holds. For aging spouses, there is the anticipation of a shared retirement, such as traveling, enjoying grandchildren, and watching sons and daughters mature and succeed in life. However, on the death of a spouse, the shared expectation which gave joy and hope is shattered. The shared dream vanishes and the landscape of life seems barren.

A father or mother paints a tableau of expected success for their children—marriage, grandchildren, career accomplishments, prosperity, and most of all happiness. But like smoke, these can disappear, and the fading of the dream of what might have been is worse than all other losses.

The challenge before us in the face of loss is not only to unearth and resurrect those dreams that are still with us, but to forge new ones. For it is in the creation of dreams that we grasp on to something to look forward to which ultimately restores hope, and it is in hope that we live life to the fullest.

Author Biographies

Ruth Wanberg-Alcorn, a former teacher, children's librarian, newspaper correspondent and graduate student at the University of California in the late sixties. Ruth, mother of five, feels she has gained enough material for story plots and poems to last a lifetime! She has established several writing groups in New Jersey and Maryland. Ruth moved to Maryland's Eastern Shore in 2006.

Sarah Barnett has had careers as a teacher, librarian and lawyer. Now retired, she lives in Rehoboth Beach, Delaware, where she writes essays and short fiction, serves as vice president of the Rehoboth Beach Writers Guild, teaches writing classes and enjoys leading "free writes" for other writers. Her work has appeared in *Delaware Beach Life, Delmarva Review* and other publications.

Jane O'Rourke Bender, 8/4/1946—9/25/2016. Jane retired to Tilghman Island, Maryland after seventeen years of employment as a clinical social worker at the Episcopal Center for Children in Washington, DC. After her retirement, along with involvement in organizations to alleviate poverty, she joined the Rehoboth Beach Writers' Guild and engaged in her lifelong love of poetry and eloquently shared her struggle with cancer—always with her wry and courageous humor.

Kimberly Blanch is a new member of the Rehoboth Beach Writers Guild and a grateful student of Judy Catterton's Memoir class. When not writing, she is a wellness consultant with twenty plus years of experience in the healing arts. She also works as an RN, serving the community at large.

Christy Walker Briedis is the retired owner of the former Rehoboth Beach boutique, Crysti. After graduating from the University of Maryland, she spent many years sailing, chartering and racing classic wooden boats. As a member of the Rehoboth Beach Writers Guild, she is now writing creative non-fiction and family memoir. A passion for nature, she splits her time between gardening in Rehoboth and skiing in Canada.

Judy Catterton retired to Delmarva after practicing law in Maryland for over 30 years. She is the 2015 recipient of a fellowship from the Delaware Division of the Arts for an emerging writer in non-fiction. She teaches essay and memoir classes for the Rehoboth Beach Writers Guild and has published a number of her own essays in several literary journals.

Terri Clifton is a writer of both fiction and nonfiction. She was awarded a fellowship by the DDoA in 2013 as an emerging artist in fiction/literature. Her short stories appear in the anthologies *Beach Days, Beach Nights*, and *The Boardwalk*. Her non-fiction work, *A Random Soldier,* was published in 2007. She resides on a historic farm along the Delaware Bay.

Ellen Collins is a writer, teacher, and artist. Her work has appeared in several journals and books, including *Bellevue Literary Review, No Place Like Here: An Anthology of Southern Delaware Poetry and Prose,* and *The Beach House.* Her first book of poetry, *The Memory Thief,* was published in 2015. She resides in Bethany Beach, DE and Vienna, VA.

Gail Braune Comorat is a founding member of Rehoboth Beach Writers' Guild, and the author of *Phases of the Moon* (Finishing Line Press). She has been published in *Adanna, Gargoyle, Grist, Mudfish, and The Widows' Handbook.* She received a 2011 Delaware Division of the Arts Fellowship Grant for Emerging Poet, and a 2015 grant for Established Poet.

Ashley Cuffee, aka Ash'iz "Tha Rebirth" is a 30-year-old poetess and Founder/Executive Director of the non-profit Beauty 4rm (pronounced, "from") Ash'iz Movement from Berlin, Maryland. She is pursuing a BA in psychology to become a Bibliotherapist, her most current endeavor is publishing her debut poetic autobiography collection.

Ginny Daly leads full lives in Rehoboth Beach, DE and Washington, DC where she hangs out with family and dogs, writes, bikes, entertains, does yoga and clowns around. First woman chairman of the Rails-to-Trails Conservancy, with lifelong career success as a writer, she also co-authored *The Guest Book* with wit and wisdom on happy houseguesting mining her long experience hostessing. (www.guestiquette.net)

Mimi S. Dupont spent years writing reportage and features for newspapers as well as advertising copy, public relations releases, organizational documents, state and national grant proposals, and parent notes to teachers. She now writes poetry, personal essays and other creative nonfiction pieces of her choice. She lives halfway between Dagsboro, Delaware and the eastern edge of the continent.

Maeke Ermarth. Completely God blessed. Retired associate broker; former CIA, Norden Systems, and GTE employee; small business owner; editor; writer, blogger; counselor/mentor; investor. Enjoy swimming, bicycling, line dancing, singing, piano, crocheting, painting, photography and life. Wife and alter-ego to Fritz Ermarth, mother, step-mother, step-grandmother, dogs and cat owner. Live in Maryland and Wyoming.

Rosa María Fernández was born in Santa Clara, Cuba and immigrated to the United States in 1965 following the communist revolution, with her parents and four siblings. She was raised in Cambridge, Maryland and has a Bachelor's of Social Work from Salisbury State College as well as a Master's from The University of Maryland School of Social Work. She currently resides in Rehoboth Beach, Delaware and is a member of The Rehoboth Beach Writer's Guild. This is her first published work.

Irene Fick's first collection of poetry, *The Stories We Tell*, was published in 2014 by The Broadkill Press. The book received first place award from the National Federation of Press Women (NFPW) and first place from the Delaware Press Association (DPA). In 2016, Irene's poem, "Asunder," received first place from DPA and second place from NFPW. Irene's poetry has been published in such journals as *Poet Lore; Gargoyle; The Broadkill Review; Philadelphia Stories; Adanna; Mojave River Review;* and *Delaware Beach Life.* Her poetry has been nominated for a Pushcart Prize. Irene lives in Lewes with her husband, Ed, and is active in the Rehoboth Beach Writers' Guild and Coastal Writers. When not writing, she sings in the CAMP Rehoboth Chorus, and supports many animal welfare organizations.

jahill aka Jane Hill, a Native New Englander, and retired mother of five has always used writing as a way to find understanding. She resides with her guide-dog on Delmarva's Eastern Shore.

Margaret Farrell Kirby is a member of the Rehoboth Beach Writers' Guild. Since retiring in 2012, she has taken classes in different genres. She has three published pieces: "Carolina Street" in *The Beach House* (2013); "Untethered" in *The Boardwalk* (2014); "Beach Daze" in *Beach Days* (2016). She is currently working on a novel.

Mary Leach recently retired from the University of Maryland. She and her husband of 51 years live in Baltimore and Bethany Beach. A mathematician by training, Mary enjoys reading, writing, traveling and playing with her grandchildren.

Faith Lord, artist and writer. Member of Rehoboth Beach Writer's Guild, as well as several art leagues, including The Ocean City Center for the Arts. "I HATE RAIN," published in 2014 *Delaware Review,* is just one stitch in her blanket of life growing up as the eldest of seven siblings.

Kathleen L. Martens, is curator of *The Divine Feminine: An Anthology of Seaside Scribes,* the literary arts complement to the women's arts exhibition, *The Divine Feminine* curated by Deborah Rolig. An active member of the Rehoboth Beach Writers Guild, her publishing credits include: the award-winning memoir of Margaret Zhao, *Really Enough, a True Story of Tyranny, Courage and Comedy*; short stories: "Molting," 2015 Judge's Choice Award; and "Flight of the Songbird," 2016 First Place winner, in the Cat and Mouse Press, *Beach Reads* anthologies, and first place winner Delaware, Press Awards, 2017 for a single short story. Kathleen has a book of short stories and two novels in process with the theme of women rising up.

Carole Schauer is a retired psychiatric nurse and lives in Ocean Pines. Traveling, volunteer work, writing, golfing, and bowling are among her many interests. She is documenting her family genealogy and writing up stories of events that occurred within the life of her family. These stories serve as the genesis for much of her writing.

Nancy Powichroski Sherman has been a teacher for over 42 years, but a writer since she was old enough to sit at her bedroom window and imagine. Her short stories have been published in *Delaware Beach Life, Fox Chase Review, Referential, The Beach House* anthology, and her own collection of stories, *Sandy Shorts.*

Irene Emily Wanberg enjoys writing & reading in her free time. Graduated with B.A. from Warren Wilson College, in North Carolina. Also did some graduate coursework in Burlington Vermont. Feels that writing called to her at an early age.

Marjorie F. Weber, a resident of Lewes, Delaware, is an active member and webmaster of the Rehoboth Beach Writers' Guild and currently serves on the Lewes Senior Center Board of Directors. In 2013, she received the Delaware Division of the Arts Emerging Artist Fellowship for creative nonfiction. She was a journalist and later a technical writer before retiring and focusing on creative writing.

Marion Winslow, former model and retired school teacher, now spends her time counting her blessings, tending her garden and writing both poetry and prose. Each January, she displays her work at the Ocean City Art League during their month-long *Shared Visions* exhibition, a collaborative effort by local visual and literary artists. Marion and Donald Winslow celebrate 63-years of wedded bliss!

Judy Wood splits her time between Washington, DC and Rehoboth, Delaware. A retired Chinese Antiques Dealer, she also spent three years living in Stockholm, Sweden as the wife of the Ambassador from the United States to Sweden. Several years ago, she joined the Rehoboth Beach Writer's Guild. When not babysitting for one of her eight grandchildren, she is writing a novel.

Sherri Wright lives in Rehoboth Beach, Delaware, after a career in education at universities and the Federal government. Running, yoga, and volunteering at a center for homeless, all figure into her writing. Her work has been published in a variety of online and print journals and recently in three books: *Our Last Walk, What I Didn't Know*, and *District Lines Volume IV*.